Best Practices in Reading

Improved Performance

LEVEL
D

© 2002 Options Publishing Inc.

able of Contents

Chain of islands that make up the Hawaiian islands

Maui

Best Practices in Reading
Level D

Product Development: Course Crafters, Inc.

Design and Production: Design 5 Creatives

Cover Design: The Quarasan Group, Inc.

Reviewer: Barbara Block, District Director of Literacy and Social Studies, Board of Education, New York City, NY

Editors: Jennifer DePino, Carolyn Thresher

Production Supervisor: Sandy Batista

Acknowledgements:
pp 96-98 "Microbes" From KIDS DISCOVER's November 2000 issue: Microbes, © 2000, Kids Discover, 149 Fifth Avenue, New York, NY 10010. All Rights Reserved. Reprinted by permission of the publisher.

pp 110-112 "Tracking the Dinosauria Family Tree: An Interview with Dino Hunter Paul Sereno" From ODYSSEY's September 2000 issue: What is a Dinosaur?, © 2000, Cobblestone Publishing Company, 30 Grove Street, Suite C, Peterborough, NH 03458. All Rights Reserved. Reprinted by permission of the publisher.

ISBN 1-56936-827-9

Options Publishing, Inc.
P.O. Box 1749
Merrimack, NH 03054-1749
TOLL FREE: 800-782-7300 • FAX: 866-424-4056

www.optionspublishing.com

All Rights Reserved. Printed in USA.

15 14 13 12 11 10 9 8 7 6

Getting Ready

OUT OF THE LIGHT, INTO THE NIGHT

BATS! They're strange, unique, and also a bit scary. They are just the kind of animal that make people wonder, "Now, where did *they* come from?" This Native American story has one answer for that question.

Think About Genre

Literature can be classified by genre (ZHON-ruh), or type. Some works are fiction—made-up stories. A folk tale is fiction from long ago. Folk tales were told rather than written down. One special kind of folk tale is the pourquoi (pur-KWAH) tale. *Pourquoi* is French for "why." In a "why" tale, the storyteller tries to explain how something came to be.

What can you expect from this kind of folk tale? Complete each sentence below so that it fits with a pourquoi tale.

This story will be set in a time that is

_____

This story will explain why

_____

Because this story is fiction, it does not tell

_____

Think About the Topic

Reread the above introduction to "Out of the Light, Into the Night." Ask yourself: *What do I know about how bats act?* List two things you know.

1._____

_____

2._____

_____

Think Ahead

Take a quick look at the story. Think about the title and illustrations. Think about what you just wrote. Make a prediction about what will happen in "Out of the Light, Into the Night."

_____

_____

Strategies:
QUESTION
MAKE INFERENCES
VISUALIZE
UNDERSTAND GENRE

QUESTION
It is a good idea to ask yourself questions as you read. If you find yourself asking, "What's happening here?" stop and try to answer your question before you continue reading.

Who's telling the story? The people in the illustration look as if they are sitting in a circle listening to a storyteller. I think it is the storyteller talking.

Why does the story-teller tell the listeners to come closer?

creature (KREE-chur)
a living thing; animal

OUT OF THE LIGHT, INTO THE NIGHT

adapted from a Native American (Anishinabe) story

You who are afraid of the night, come closer. Sit as near to the bright fire as you dare. Now look to your right and to your left. Your friends are near you, are they not? So you can see that you have nothing to fear. It is important that you are not afraid here in the night. And it is important that you understand this: The night **creature** I will tell about is not to be feared, either.

Just as you rise with the Sun and sleep when he sleeps, so do many of the creatures of the forest. That's why it was so strange one morning long ago when the Sun's light did not shine. Owl did not mind, for she hunts at night. But those who flee her claws were worn out and wondered out loud.

"Where is the Sun?" asked the field mouse and a little green frog. Soon even the birds and the animals that hunt by day understood that somehow the Sun was missing.

It was a small brown squirrel who found the missing Sun.

High up in the branches above the forest floor, the squirrel could see for miles. At first it saw only darkness. But finally, far off to the east, it saw a glow.

Hopping from tree to tree, the squirrel climbed closer and closer to the light. When it was very close, it saw that the glow came from the Sun. But the Sun was weak and pale. The Sun had become caught in the branches of a very high tree. The harder he tried to free himself, the more tangled he got.

The Sun begged the squirrel, "Help me!"

The squirrel thought about what it could do to help. Then, using its sharp teeth, it began to bite at one of the branches that held the Sun. Soon the squirrel had bitten clear through it.

The Sun sighed. "That's good. Keep working."

The squirrel moved from branch to branch, **gnawing** away. It was warm work, though. Each time the Sun broke free from another branch, it grew stronger and hotter.

"I must stop," said the squirrel. "I'm burning!"

It was true. The heat from the Sun had turned the little brown squirrel's fur to the color of ashes.

"Don't stop!" said the Sun. "I'm almost free."

Again the squirrel listened to the Sun's plea. Again it freed another branch. And again the Sun grew still hotter.

MAKE INFERENCES

Sometimes authors give clues instead of directly telling you something. You have to use the clues and what you already know to figure out what the author is saying.

> The Sun is weak and pale. He must have used up all his strength while trying to get out of the branches of the tree.

The squirrel keeps working even though it is getting burned by the Sun. What does this tell you about the squirrel?

gnawing (NAW-ing) biting and chewing

© 2002 Options Publishing Inc.

height (HITE)
how high something is

"I'm burning from the heat," said the squirrel. "Even my tail has burned away!"

"Just a little more," pleaded the Sun. "A little more!"

Once more the squirrel went to work. It was nearly blind from the brightness of the Sun, but it sensed when the Sun was finally freed from the branches. Soon the Sun was riding high in the sky, where it was supposed to be.

Even from that height, though, Sun could see the poor squirrel. Gone were its bushy tail and the brown fur that had covered its body and his eyes were closed against the brightness of the Sun.

"Poor thing," said the Sun. "You helped me, and now I will help you. What one thing have you wanted to do all your life?"

"Fly," was the squirrel's simple answer.

"Then so you shall. But you will fly only at night, when you won't have to face my bright light."

With that, the creature that had once been a squirrel spread its new wings and began to fly. And so it does every night when the Sun goes down in the west. For that is how the first bat came to be.

Visualize

Think about the elements, or parts,
that go together to form "Out of the Light,
Into the Night." Fill in these elements in the story map below.
(Some elements are already filled in.) Reread the folk tale if you need to.

Title

_____

Characters

_____

Setting

Place: _____

Time: long ago

Problem

_____

_____

Event 1

_____

_____

Event 2

_____

_____

Event 3

The squirrel frees the
Sun, but its fur is
burned, it loses its tail,
and it is nearly blinded.

Ending

_____

_____

Sharing Fiction

Summarize

You can be a storyteller, too. Sometimes when you read a story that you really like, you want to tell your friends or family about it. You can give them a summary, or short version, of the story.

In the space below, write a summary of the story. Use your story map to help you remember the important parts of the story.

_____

_____

_____

_____

First I'll tell them what kind of story it is and where and when it takes place. Then I'll say who the main characters are and tell what they were trying to do. I'll end by saying how the story turned out and what happened to the characters.

Determine What Is Important

This is another good strategy to use after you finish reading a story. Ask yourself:

- What ideas are important to remember when you recall the story?
- What details are unimportant and can be left out?

Read each statement below. Fill in the bubble beside each one that identifies something important from the story. More than one answer can be correct.

Ⓐ Some people are afraid of the night.

Ⓑ One morning the Sun did not rise.

Ⓒ A little squirrel went looking for the Sun.

Ⓓ The green frog wondered where the Sun was.

Look through the story again. What is another important idea?

_____

_____

_____

Getting Ready

People have lots of ideas about bats—but how many of these ideas are really true? You may be surprised at what you don't know about these amazing animals!

The Truth About Bats

Think About Genre

You know that works of fiction have made-up characters and actions. If you want to learn facts about real people, places, things, and animals, you read nonfiction. The informational article you are about to read is classified as nonfiction.

Most informational articles are written in a similar way. They follow a certain form and include such features, or items, as those listed below. Take a quick look at "The Truth About Bats." Which features does it contain? Fill in the bubble beside each possible answer.

Ⓐ photographs with informative captions

Ⓑ information based on facts about a topic

Ⓒ a structure that lets you compare and contrast fact and fiction

Ⓓ graphic aids, such as diagrams

Think About the Topic

Reread the introduction to "The Truth About Bats." What did you read in "Out of the Light, Into the Night" that sounds like information you have heard before? Write two ideas about bats that you want to check—are they true?

1._____

_____

2._____

_____

Think Ahead

Think about what you noticed when you scanned the article. Think about the title. Now make a prediction. What do you think you will learn as you read "The Truth About Bats"?

_____

_____

_____

_____

The Truth About Bats

MAKE CONNECTIONS

For nonfiction authors to help you learn new information, they make connections to things you already know.

I think the author wants me to think about what I already know about bats in order to answer some questions.

QUESTION

Before you answer question 2, ask . . . Have I ever seen or heard of bats flying around during the day? At night? Write what you know about bats. Think about your own experience, stories you have read, and movies you have seen.

_____

_____

_____

_____

You have probably heard the words "blind as a bat" hundreds of times. It is a phrase that is so familiar that few people question it. But is it true? Are bats really blind? Or is this one of those sayings that has been repeated so many times that everyone *thinks* it is true?

As a matter of fact, it is *not* true. Bats have good eyesight. Now, doesn't that make you wonder how much you really know about these interesting creatures? To test yourself, read each statement and decide if it is true or false. Then compare what you *think* you know about bats to the facts at the end of the article.

Little brown bats are common in North America.

1. You should cover your head around bats, because they can get tangled in your hair. **True False**

2. All bats are nocturnal; that is, they are active only at night. **True False**

3. Bats are helpful to humans because they eat many harmful insects. **True False**

4. All bats have dark coloring, like the night. **True False**

5. Bats are the only flying mammals. **True False**

The male red bat, which lives in North America, is bright red, while the female has a grayish-red coat.

UNDERSTAND GENRE
(informational article)

This article takes everyday ideas about bats and tells whether they are true.

I can compare and contrast what I know about bats and what is really true.

6. All bats are about the size of a common pigeon. **True False**

7. Bats can carry rabies. **True False**

8. Bats are vampires and live on the blood of humans. **True False**

9. Bats hang upside-down when they are resting. **True False**

List two pieces of information that turned out to be true after all.

_____

_____

_____

_____

ANSWERS

1. **False.** That is just an old tale. Bats are not interested in your hair—unless you are wearing a nest of insects on your head that might attract a hungry bat!

2. **True**, mostly. Most bats are nocturnal. However, some are crepuscular, that is, they are active at twilight.

3. **True.** If there are lots of bats in your area, it may be because they are attracted to the large number of insects there.

4. **False.** There are brown bats and black bats. But, depending on where they live, bats may have bright colors and markings—even yellow, red, and silver.

5. **True.** Bats are mammals (like cats, dogs, and people). All other flying creatures are birds or insects.

crepuscular
(krih PUS-kyuh-lahr) active at dawn or twilight

rabies (RAY-beez) a deadly disease, caused by a virus, that can affect warm-blooded animals, such as humans, dogs, and horses.

Asking questions can help you with fiction and nonfiction. Remember to ask yourself questions as you read: *Who? What? When? Where? Why? How?*

What do vampire bats live on mostly? According to the article, they live on the blood of other animals.

What are my chances of being bitten by a vampire bat? Why?

_____

_____

_____

_____

wingspan the distance (span) between the tip of one wing to the tip of the other when the wings are spread out

6. **False.** The smallest bat is about the size of a bumble bee. The largest has a wingspan of five feet (1.5 meters). Most bats in North America have a wingspan of about 12 inches (30 centimeters).

7. **True.** Bats are a warm-blooded animal, so a bite from a bat carrying rabies can be deadly. That is why it is important to never handle a bat.

8. **False.** There is a vampire bat, which feeds on the blood of other animals, such as cattle. It does not live in North America. It rarely bites human beings.

9. **True.** Even baby bats can rest this way. Bats do not build nests, so a baby bat holds on to its mother until it is ready to fly and can hang upside-down by itself.

Did you learn something new about bats from taking this quiz? If you like, you can learn even more. Here are some key words you can use to do some research on Chiroptera (ky-ROP-tu-ruh)—that is the scientific name for bats:

KEY WORDS

- brown bats
- echolocation
- flying foxes
- free-tailed bats
- Organization for Bat Conservation
- ultrasonic sound

What features of the bat's skeleton remind you of other mammals? For example, in bats, arms and fingers have become wings.

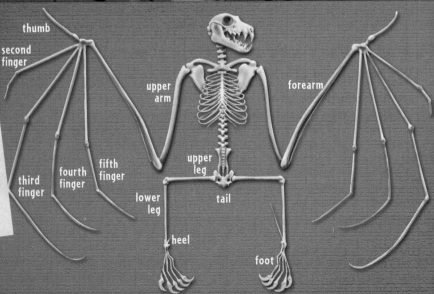

thumb
second finger
upper arm
forearm
third finger
fourth finger
fifth finger
upper leg
lower leg
tail
heel
foot

Understanding Nonfiction

The Truth About Bats

Visualize

The information in this article is presented in an unusual way. First there are the numbered statements, which can be either True or False. The correct information is at the end of the article.

Use this chart to organize the information you learned in "The Truth About Bats." Decide how to categorize each true-false statement. Is it completely true? Is it completely false? Is it usually, but not always, true?

Write each statement where it belongs. Go back to the article to find the information.

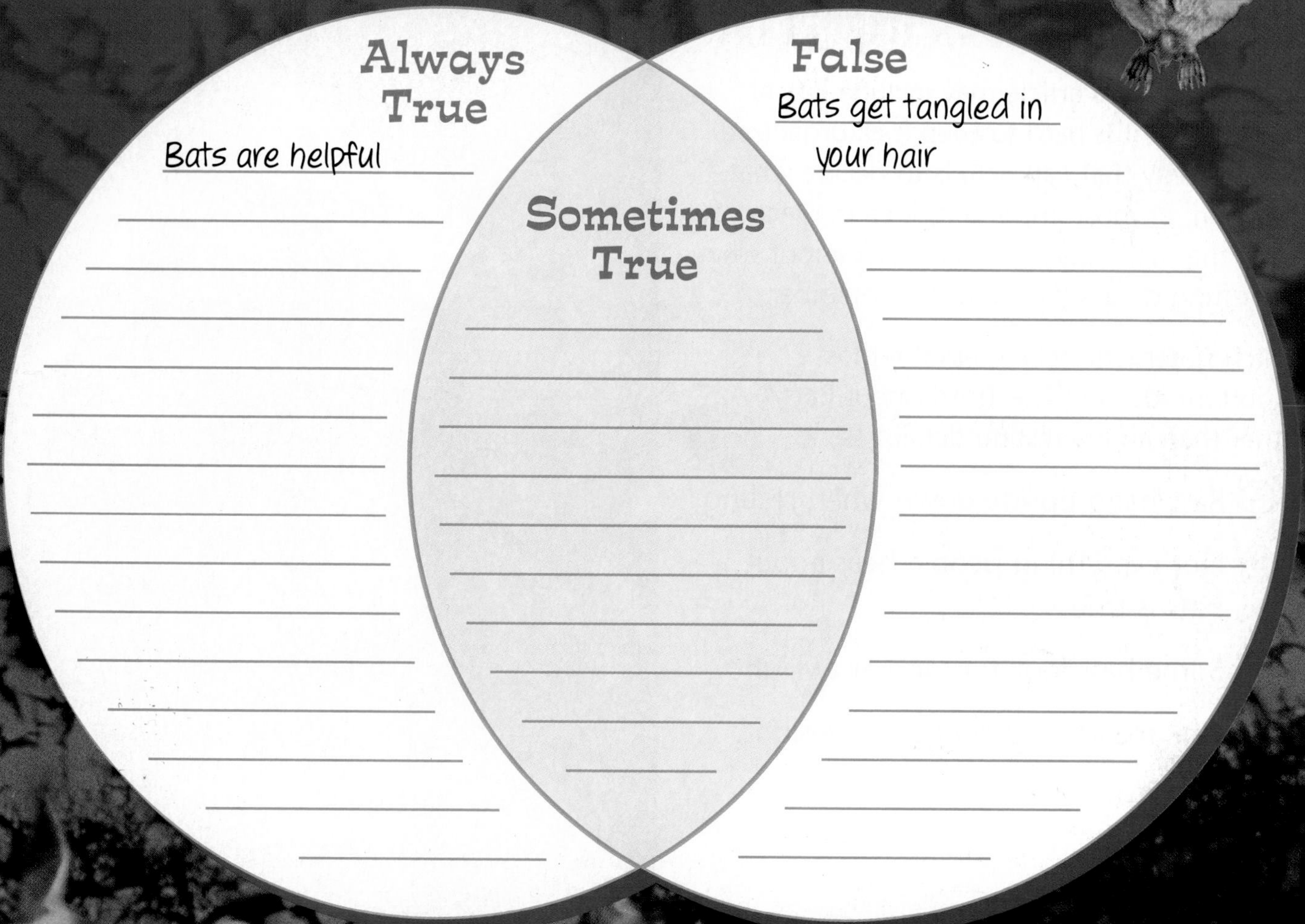

Always True

Bats are helpful

Sometimes True

False

Bats get tangled in your hair

Summarize

Now that you know something about bats, you may want to test your friends to see what they know about bats. Summarizing the article can help you remember what to include in your test.

Summarize the information in "The Truth About Bats." Use the information in your chart to help you.

> My summary will start with the name of the article and an explanation of how the information is organized. Then I'll tell which facts are true and which are not.

_____

_____

_____

_____

_____

Determine What Is Important

An informational article may include lots of information. It is hard to keep it all organized. One strategy that can help is to decide what the main, or most important, idea is. Once you know the main idea, you can think about what interesting details you want to remember.

Which statement below tells the most important idea in "The Truth About Bats," rather than an interesting detail.

(A) Bats hang upside-down when resting.

(B) Not everything people hear about bats is true.

(C) Some bats look for food at twilight.

(D) Bats may have very good eyesight.

OUT OF THE LIGHT, INTO THE NIGHT

The Truth About Bats

Make Connections

The following questions will help you connect what you already knew about bats with what you read.

1. What did you know about bats before you read "Out of the Light, Into the Night" and "The Truth About Bats"?

_____

_____

_____

_____

_____

2. What did you learn from reading the selections? Explain.

_____

_____

_____

_____

_____

3. Why do you think it is important to know the truth about an animal like the bat?

_____

_____

_____

_____

_____

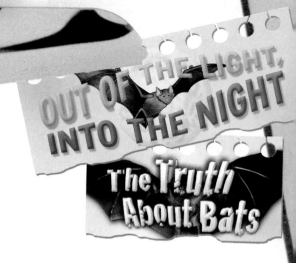

OUT OF THE LIGHT, INTO THE NIGHT

The Truth About Bats

Write a Persuasive Letter

Write a letter to an organization that tries to protect bats. Tell how you feel about bats now that you have read these two selections. Explain why you feel bats should be protected.

_____

_____

_____

_____

_____

_____

_____

BLACKLINE MASTER Before you write, use the Blackline Master your teacher will give you to plan your persuasive letter.

Plan Your Research

Study the key words at the end of the nonfiction article. Choose one or two you would like to learn more about. Make a list of questions that you would like to have answered when you look these words up.

Little brown bat in flight

Key Words	Questions

Net Connection

http://www.members.aol.com/bats4kids2/help.html

Getting Ready

LIGHT UP THE TOWN

**Did you ever wonder what life was like before electric lights?
Well, sometimes it was very dangerous! The year is 1899. How can reporter
Emily Nash make her readers understand that using electric lights can save lives?**

Think About Genre

One kind of fiction uses real people, places, and events in a story about make-believe characters. This genre is called historical fiction. The author had to research the historical setting (time and place) to make it true-to-life. When you read historical fiction, you step into the past.

Fill in the bubble beside each statement that tells something you might find in historical fiction.

(A) Some people, places, and events will be real.

(B) All the people, places, and events will be real.

(C) You see how people lived in a particular time and place.

(D) Everything in the story is a historical fact.

Think About the Topic

Reread the introduction to "Light Up the Town." Ask yourself: *What do I know about how people lit their homes without electricity? What were the dangers?* Write two things you know on the lines below.

1._____

_____

_____

2._____

_____

_____

Think Ahead

Look at the story and illustrations. Reread the title. Think about what you just wrote and predict what you think will happen in "Light Up the Town." Fill in the bubbles next to each statement that matches your predictions.

(A) A reporter writes a story about a burned doll.

(B) A reporter starts a fire.

(C) A reporter wants people to use electric lights.

(D) Electric lights cause a fire.

Strategies:
VISUALIZE
MAKE INFERENCES
QUESTION
UNDERSTAND GENRE

LIGHT UP  THE TOWN

LIGHT UP THE TOWN

VISUALIZE

Look for words that set the scene. The words tell about characters, place, and time.

> I need to look for details that help me picture the scene. I know the story is set in 1899. Two people are talking.

Where does the story take place? Who are the characters?

incandescent lamp (in-kan-DES-ent lamp) light bulb that is powered by electricity

kerosene lamp (KEH-ruh-seen lamp) glass-enclosed lamp that burns oil

"Emily, I have an assignment for you," said Elijah Brown, publisher of *The Valley News*. "You're going to cover last night's fire at the furniture factory."

Emily grabbed her shawl, hat, and gloves, and then her pad and pencil. She headed for the door.

"Wait," Brown continued. "Here's the story I want—electricity saves lives. How many more fires will start because folks still light their homes with kerosene lamps or gas lamps? The incandescent lamp has been around for more than twenty years. But folks aren't changing over fast enough." Elijah paced, his shoes clumping on the bare wood.

Brown enjoyed his local fame as an independent thinker. For example, he didn't like people telling him whom he could and could not hire. The proof of that was when he employed Emily Nash as a junior reporter.

"The Fire Marshall says a leak in the gas line and a spark caused this fire. It was more like an explosion. A cottage next to the factory burned to the ground, too. The family who lived there was lucky to escape. And thank goodness all the factory workers had gone home." He spoke excitedly. "Do we have to wait until there's a real tragedy before people will change? Emily, get me a story! I want readers begging for electric lights by the time they finish your article."

The Valley News had a carriage and driver to take reporters quickly to the scene of a news story. "Snead's factory," Emily told the driver. The horses set off at a brisk trot.

Emily enjoyed hurrying around town to cover the news, though some were shocked by her independence. Her father and Elijah Brown had grown up together. Besides, in this small community where everyone knew each other, Emily's love of writing was legend. Most folks accepted her unusual career.

Snead's Furniture Factory was a charred, ruined frame on that October morning. Mr. Snead was examining the damage.

A stone foundation was all that remained of the burnt cottage. The husband and wife raked through the **rubble**, looking for any objects they could save. A girl about eight years old sat nearby on a log, sadly rocking a half-burned doll. Its clothes were covered in soot. Its **porcelain** head was badly cracked. Emily walked over to her.

porcelain
(POR-suh-lin) very fine China, often used in the past for the heads and hands of dolls

rubble
(RUH-bul) pile of broken rock, glass, wood, and other building material

Why does Emily talk to the little girl? I think the girl and her doll will be part of Emily's story.

Why were the girl and doll at the scene of the fire? What might Emily be trying to say by putting her in the story?

UNDERSTAND GENRE
(historical fiction)

What are some details the author includes that show the story took place in the past?

typewriter
(TIEP-rie-tur) Machine that prints individual letters on paper

"How's she doing?" Emily asked. The girl looked up for a moment, but then hung her head, blinking rapidly. "I'm a reporter for *The Valley News*. Have you ever read it?"

The girl shook her head.

Emily continued. "I want these fires to stop. I'm letting people know there's a safer way to light our homes at night. Can I tell about you and your doll in my article? What's her name?"

"Barbara," the girl whispered.

Emily and the girl talked as Emily took notes on the pad. At last, Emily shook the girl's hand and stood up. "Thank you," Emily said. "Maybe this article will change people's minds."

Back at the office Emily grabbed a sheet of paper, rolled it into the **typewriter** and typed the article. Then she made a few pencil corrections and handed the finished piece to Elijah Brown. He read it, and then gave Emily a long, hard look. "So the victim of this fire was—a porcelain doll?" The reporter nodded nervously. A smile spread across Elijah Brown's face.

"Emily, this article will go straight to the heart. Put in the address of the power company so people will know how to get electric lighting. We can still rush this into the evening paper. I think there's a bright future ahead for our town."

Visualize

LIGHT UP THE TOWN

Think about Emily Nash and Elijah Brown, the main characters in this story. Write words that describe each character in the boxes. Look back in "Light Up the Town" for ideas. Then, choose two boxes for each character. Find examples in the story to support the words you chose. Write your examples on the lines below.

Emily Nash

caring

Elijah Brown

Wants progress

_____

_____

_____

_____

wants progress —Elijah Brown wants people to get electric lighting.

_____

_____

_____

Summarize

After you read a story, you usually know how you felt about it. But do you know why? Summarizing the main points helps you think about the entire story.

Look at the sentences. Put a check in the box next to the main points you would include in a summary of "Light Up the Town."

□ There has been a fire in town.

□ Elijah Brown has a mustache.

□ Elijah Brown assigns Emily Nash to write an article about the fire.

□ The article's purpose is to convince readers to use electric lights.

□ Emily Nash meets an eight-year-old girl whose family has lost their home in the fire.

□ Elijah Brown prints Emily's story.

□ Emily Nash includes the address of the power company in her article.

LIGHT UP THE TOWN

> I'll think about the story problem, the important events, and what happened at the end of the story. These remind me of the main points I can put in my summary.

Determine What Is Important

When news reporters like Emily Nash write a story for a newspaper, they have to tell who, what, where, when, why, and how. Decide which details are important about the factory fire. On the lines write a few important details from the story to answer each question.

Who?_____

What?_____

Where?_____

When?_____

Why?_____

How?_____

Getting Ready

A light bulb has stayed lit for 100 years and is still going strong. How can this be, you ask? Read on, and find out some "bright ideas" about light bulbs!

Don't Make Light of This!

Think About Genre

Literature can be fiction, like "Light Up the Town," or nonfiction, where the writing provides facts about a topic. In nonfiction, the people, places, and events are all real.

Nonfiction articles are called informational articles. They tell you about one topic. This is the kind of article you may find in a magazine. Informational articles often include diagrams, charts, photographs, and captions. They are included to help you better understand the topic. Also, informational articles are often divided into sections, each with its own heading.

Look quickly through the article, "Don't Make Light of This!" Which of the following features do you see? Fill in the bubble next to each one you see.

Ⓐ labeled diagrams

Ⓑ headings that guide you to different parts of the article

Ⓒ details about how something works

Ⓓ maps and graphs

Think About the Topic

Reread the introduction to this informational article. Ask yourself, *What can I tell about the topic from these sentences? What did I learn about light in the story, "Light Up the Town"?* Write a sentence that tells about the topic. Then write two sentences that tell what you learned from the story about this topic.

_____

_____

_____

_____

Think Ahead

Make a prediction of what you think this article will be about. Think about the title, headings, photos, diagrams, and captions.

_____

_____

_____

_____

This is the uniform that Livermore's volunteer fire fighters wore in 1901. The fire alarm that called them was a bell.

QUESTION

Asking questions while you read can help you better understand an article. When you ask questions, you need to read the text carefully to find the answers.

I wonder why more people had lights in cities than outside of cities? I should read further and think about what I already know to find the answer.

Think about how cities are set up and what is needed for electricity to work. Why do you think people long ago who lived in cities had more electric lights than people living outside of cities?

How "The Bulb" Got Its Job

Few people outside of big cities had electric lights back in 1901. Gaslight and lamplight were used. "The bulb" was a gift to the Livermore Fire Department in 1901 from Dennis Bernal, who owned the power company.

He donated it as a kind of night-light for the "Fire Boys," Livermore's volunteer firefighters. "The bulb's" dull, orange-y glow threw enough light to let the firefighters find their equipment at night without tripping over it. "He just did nice little things like that," recalled his daughter, Zylpha Bernal Beck.

Years passed. Electricity and electric lights became part of everyday life, and "the bulb" still burned. By 1974, it was named in the *Guinness Book of World Records* as possibly the longest-burning bulb. It was also featured in a Ripley's "Believe it Or Not" cartoon strip. President George W. Bush and California Senator Barbara Boxer sent birthday wishes at the time of "the bulb's" centennial celebration.

What's the Fascination?

What's the attraction? Perhaps this little light bulb helps people imagine what life was like a hundred years ago. It reminds us that there was a time before electric appliances and machines were a part of our daily lives.

Will it ever stop working? Most likely. Ripley's "Believe It or Not" museum in San Francisco has asked to own "the bulb" after it burns out. But who knows? In another 100 years, a whole new group of people may be singing "Happy Birthday" to a light bulb that just won't quit!

ACCORDING TO GUINNESS

MOST DURABLE LIGHT

The average light bulb lasts for 750 to 1,000 hours. There is some evidence that a carbon filament bulb burning in the fire department, Livermore, Alameda County, California has been burning since 1901.

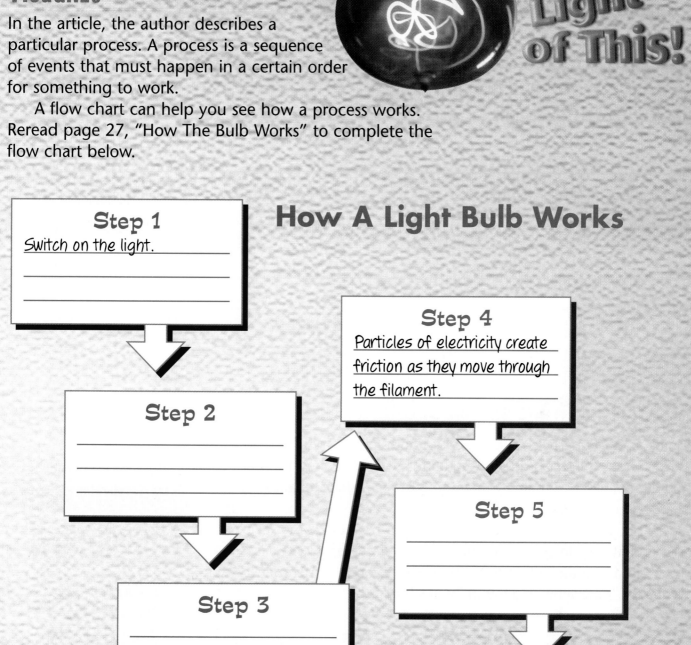

Understanding Nonfiction

Visualize

In the article, the author describes a particular process. A process is a sequence of events that must happen in a certain order for something to work.

A flow chart can help you see how a process works. Reread page 27, "How The Bulb Works" to complete the flow chart below.

Don't Make Light of This!

How A Light Bulb Works

Step 1
Switch on the light.
_____
_____

Step 2
_____
_____
_____

Step 3
_____
_____
_____

Step 4
Particles of electricity create friction as they move through the filament.

Step 5
_____
_____
_____

Conclusion
We use the light.
_____
_____

Don't Make Light of This!

Summarize

After you read an article, parts of it still may be unclear to you. Summarizing is one way to think back about the information and put it in order.

As briefly as possible, summarize "Don't Make Light of This!" Use the section headings to guide you.

_____

_____

_____

_____

_____

_____

_____

> I'll start my summary with the title. Then I'll use the section headings as main topics. I'll look for details to support each main topic.

Determine What Is Important

Think about the article, "Don't Make Light of This!" What things stick in your mind? Some of these things may be interesting details you liked. Some may be important ideas that the author wants you to remember.

On the lines below, list four pieces of information from the article that stick in your mind. Beside each statement, write *I* if it's an important idea that the author wants you to remember. Write *D* if it's a detail you found interesting.

_____

_____

_____

_____

_____

100 watt Shelby Mazda Lamp in Shelby Museum, Shelby, Ohio

Make Connections

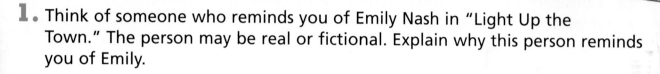

Think about what you read in "Light Up the Town" and "Don't Make Light of This!" Think about how they connect to other things that you have read or heard, to what you have experienced, and to the world around you.

1. Think of someone who reminds you of Emily Nash in "Light Up the Town." The person may be real or fictional. Explain why this person reminds you of Emily.

_____

_____

2. "Light Up the Town" is fiction, while "Don't Make Light of This!" is nonfiction. In what ways are these two selections alike?

_____

_____

_____

Inventor Thomas Edison showing the incandescent lamps he created.

3. How is the Livermore Bulb like a light bulb in your house? How is it different?

_____

_____

_____

4. What danger did people face when lighting their homes before there were electric lights? What dangers do people face today with electricity?

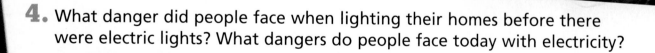

_____

_____

_____

Putting Fiction And Nonfiction Together

Write an Eyewitness Account

Imagine you witnessed the furniture factory fire that destroyed the cottage next door. Write an account of what you saw, heard, smelled, and felt. Use descriptive words in your paragraph. Remember to answer the questions *Who? What? When? Where? Why?* and *How?* Think about what you read in "Light Up the Town" and "Don't Make Light of This!" to help you.

_____

_____

_____

_____

BLACKLINE MASTER Before you write, use the Blackline Master your teacher will give you to plan your eyewitness account.

Plan Your Research

Think of another long-ago invention, such as the automobile or telephone, that changed people's lives in a big way. List three questions you would want answered about the early days of this invention.

_____

_____

_____

_____

_____

Net Connection

http://www.centennialbulb.org

http://www.rootsweb.com/~ohscogs/shelbymuseum/ShelbyMuseum3.ht

Getting Ready

SECRET OF THE SEA

No human being has ever seen a giant squid—alive. In this adventure story, a scientist hopes to change all that. She willingly faces danger if it will lead her to this strange and mysterious monster of the deep.

Think About Genre

Literature can be classified by genre (ZHON-ruh). Some works are fiction. Fictional stories are made up by authors. Just because they are made up, though, doesn't mean they don't include real facts and details. "Secret of the Sea" is one kind of fiction— an adventure story.

What do you expect from an adventure story? Fill in the bubble beside each statement that you think fits an adventure story.

Ⓐ It is filled with suspense.

Ⓑ It is quiet and peaceful.

Ⓒ The main character takes a risk to gain something important.

Ⓓ It is filled with silly events that make the reader laugh.

Think About the Topic

Reread the above introduction to "Secret of the Sea." Ask yourself: *What do I know about life in the deep ocean? What do I know about squids? What do I know about scientists who explore the ocean?* Write two things you know on the lines below.

_____

_____

_____

Think Ahead

Take a quick look at the story. Think about the title and illustrations. Think about what you wrote on the topic. Make a prediction—tell what you think you will read about in "Secret of the Sea."

_____

_____

_____

Reading Fiction

Strategies:
QUESTION
MAKE INFERENCES
UNDERSTAND GENRE
VISUALIZE

QUESTION

Ask yourself questions as you read: *Who? What? When? Why? How? What if?*

Who's talking in the first two sentences? Wait, I can use the names mentioned. Dr. Abbott is speaking to Dr. Lopez, and Dr. Lopez is answering.

What does Dr. Abbott mean?

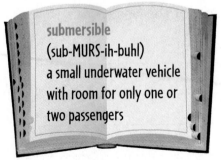

submersible
(sub-MURS-ih-buhl)
a small underwater vehicle with room for only one or two passengers

"Dr. Lopez, can you hear me?"

"Yes, Dr. Abbott. Everything is fine down here."

Explorer, the **submersible**, sank deeper into the ocean. All light from above disappeared. It became so dark that Dr. Lopez, who was piloting the submersible, couldn't even see the controls. She felt them with her hands. When she located the switch, she flicked on the spotlights. She saw hundreds of fish swimming around her. Pearlsides, no bigger than her finger, zipped past and disappeared. Lantern fish darted in and out of the spheres of light.

"What do you see, Dr. Lopez? Any sign of the giant squid?" Dr. Abbott's voice was hopeful. This was the last day of their research mission. So far, they hadn't seen the giant squid.

"No sign yet, but I'm not quite deep enough," Dr. Lopez answered. "I'm turning on the cameras now."

On the boat above, Dr. Abbott and the research team gathered around the video screens. Each one watched the images from one of the cameras on the *Explorer*.

"We have visual," Dr. Abbott told Dr. Lopez. "We're right there with you."

There was a comfortable silence. Dr. Lopez watched a few silvery hoki pass by. They were big, nearly three feet long, but much smaller than a giant squid. The animal she was searching for was fifty or sixty feet long!

Suddenly, Dr. Lopez heard a clicking noise.

"Shhh," she said. "Listen."

Dr. Abbott and the team leaned in to the microphone. They heard a series of fast clicks followed by a few slow ones. The clicks kept coming. It sounded as if someone were tapping on the bottom of an empty can.

"We've got a sperm whale!" Dr. Lopez yelled.

"That's a great sign," Dr. Abbott said to the research team. "Sperm whales love to eat giant squids. If there's a sperm whale down here, there might be a giant squid near by." She stared closely at the video screen.

"Do you see the whale?" someone on the research team asked.

Dr. Lopez looked around. She knew many people would find it spooky down here in the ocean all alone, but not her. She felt at home, as if she were a fish.

"Yes, just ahead." She maneuvered the *Explorer* so that the camera would see the whale. It was deep brownish-gray with a pale underbelly. Just then it turned. The scientists saw the telltale sucker marks left by a giant squid.

"Wow! Look at those sucker marks!" Dr. Lopez exclaimed. This whale has obviously been feeding on a giant squid."

The whale disappeared in the dark water.

MAKE INFERENCES
Sometimes authors show rather than tell. They expect you to "read between the lines."

If Dr. Lopez knows it's a sperm whale, then sperm whales must make that clicking sound she's hearing.

Note how most people feel being alone in the deep ocean. How does Dr. Lopez feel? What does this tell you about her?

How does the author build suspense in this part of the story?

VISUALIZE

If there are no pictures to help you see what's happening, make your own "mind pictures."

Dr. Lopez says that the squid is about 60 feet long. Picture how big that is. What else is about 60 feet long?

tentacle (TEN-tah-kuhl) a long snake-like arm; squids (and octopuses) have tentacles that are covered with suckers

"Dr. Abbott, I've reached the ocean floor. I'm going to move along the bottom for a bit. Keep your eyes open. I feel like we're close to something."

"Dr. Lopez?" Dr. Abbott said after a few minutes. There was no answer.

"Dr. Lopez?" Dr. Abbott sounded concerned. Dr. Lopez was at least 2,000 feet underwater. No one had ever taken a submersible that deep in the ocean before. It was a dangerous mission.

"Dr. Lopez!" Dr. Abbott called fearfully.

Finally, Dr. Lopez answered. "I'm all right!" She sounded excited.

"I see it!" she exclaimed. "Look. Straight ahead. A giant squid is right in front of me. It's got to be sixty feet long!"

Moments later, the squid appeared on the video screen. Its eight long arms danced gracefully in the water. As the team watched, one of its two feeding tentacles reached out and grabbed a hoki. Dr. Abbott gasped. This was the most amazing animal she had ever seen!

"Look at the eyes!" Dr. Lopez called. "They're bigger than basketballs. And those tentacles must be forty feet long! This is it, everybody!"

She could hear the team cheering 2,000 feet above her.

Visualize

Think about how the author put the story together.

Look back in "Secret of the Sea" to find the information you need to fill in this story map.

Title
_____

Characters
Dr. Abbott _____
_____
_____

Setting
_____
_____
_____

Problem
A team of scientists wants to find and observe the mysterious giant squid.

Important Event
_____
_____
_____
_____

Conclusion
_____
_____

Summarize

Once you have read a story, a friend
might ask you what it was about. A good
way to answer is to give a summary of the story.

As briefly as possible, summarize what happened
in "Secret of the Sea." Use every key element from
your story map to help you.

_____

_____

_____

_____

_____

_____

> First, I'll name
> the story and the
> main characters. After I tell
> where the story takes place, I'll
> explain what the story is about.
> Then I'll tell the other
> important events, including the
> conclusion at the end
> of the story.

Determine What Is Important

This is another good strategy to use after you finish reading a story.
What ideas are important to remember when you recall the story?
What details are unimportant and can be left out?

Read each statement. Fill in the bubble beside each statement
that identifies something important from the story.

(A) Dr. Lopez is a scientist who is studying giant squids.

(B) Dr. Lopez sees pearlsides and lantern fish.

(C) Hoki are bigger than pearlsides but much smaller than giant squids.

(D) Dr. Lopez sees a sperm whale with sucker marks on it.

Look through the story for another important idea. Write it below.

_____

_____

_____

_____

Getting Ready

Giant squids sound like they could be found only in horror movies and adventure tales—but they actually exist! Find out about the "real thing."

The Search For The Giant Squid

Think About Genre

As you know, literature can be classified by genre. Some works are fiction, like "Secret of the Sea." Other works are nonfiction. They tell facts about real people, places, and things. The nonfiction you are about to read is an informational article. It doesn't tell a story. Instead, it provides information about a particular topic.

Informational articles follow a certain form and usually include some of the items, or features, listed below. Take a quick look at the article "The Search for the Giant Squid." Which features does it contain? Fill in the bubble beside each one.

Ⓐ photographs or realistic artwork

Ⓑ captions that provide extra information

Ⓒ headings that tell about each section in the article

Ⓓ graphic aids such as maps, graphs, charts, diagrams, or time lines

Ⓔ directions or steps in a process

Think About the Topic

Reread the above introduction to "The Search for the Giant Squid." Ask yourself: *What did I learn about giant squids from reading "Secret of the Sea"?* Write two things you found out on the lines below.

_____

_____

_____

_____

_____

Think Ahead

Now that you have looked at the article, think about the title and the features. Make a prediction—tell what you think you will learn as you read "The Search for the Giant Squid."

_____

_____

_____

_____

The Search For The Giant Squid

MAKE CONNECTIONS

Nonfiction authors often connect new information to familiar information that readers know.

> Now I know how big a giant squid's eyes are, since I know the size of a basketball.

What other comparisons does the author include to help you understand what a giant squid looks like?

_____

_____

_____

_____

_____

barbed (barbd) covered with sharp, needlelike hairs, or barbs

What Is *Architeuthis dux*? And Why Is It So Interesting?

Architeuthis dux—that's the scientific name for the giant squid. It's an enormous, mysterious-looking animal that lives in the ocean. Like us, it has two eyes, but its eyes are the size of basketballs. Like an octopus, it has eight powerful arms covered with barbed suckers. It also has two feeding tentacles that are three to four times longer than the eight arms. The giant squid's mouth has a beak like a parrot and a toothed tongue called a *radula*. You don't want to get caught in that mouth!

The largest specimen of giant squid ever measured was 60 feet long. It was measured from the tip of its torpedo-shaped body to the end of its tentacles. Scientists believe a giant squid can grow as long as 75 feet. They also believe a full-grown squid can weigh over a ton. That's as much as a walrus, a bison, or two medium-sized polar bears.

Why Is the Giant Squid a Mystery?

Amazingly, no one has ever seen a living giant squid in its natural habitat—the deepest part of the ocean. It seems like we would see it often. It's a huge animal. We see

Below is the AUV (autonomous underwater vehicle). In 1999, Dr. Roper and his team used it to search for a giant squid.

Dr. Clyde Roper

whales all the time. How could we miss this squid?

There are a couple of reasons. First, oceans are gigantic. They stretch for thousands of miles between continents. Even a huge animal, like a giant squid, can stay hidden. Second, giant squids inhabit the deepest parts of the ocean. Scientists believe they probably live between 660 and 2,300 feet below the surface. That means they can hide half a mile under the water. That's deep! What can scientists do?

How Are Scientists Searching for the Giant Squid?

If scientists want to find giant squids, they have to search down deep. Dr. Clyde Roper is an invertebrate zoologist at the Smithsonian Institution in Washington, D.C. He has led two expeditions using new equipment that can travel to the ocean floor. Both times, he and his team explored the deep-sea world of Kaikora Canyon in New Zealand.

In 1997, Dr. Roper and his team used *Odyssey*, a 430-pound machine that looks like a blimp. It has a computer-controlled camera and is programmed to travel by itself.

invertebrate zoologist (in-VER-tih-brit zoh-AH-luh-jist) a scientist who studies animals without backbones

Ask yourself questions about the information in the article: *Who? What? Why? When? How?*

> How could squids get caught in fishermen's nets if they live down so deep? I'll bet they come up to feed on all the fish in the net.

Why do large animals need bones or some other kind of framework? What do you think would happen to a giant squid without a gladius to support it?

_____

_____

_____

_____

_____

_____

specimen (SPES-ih-men)
One member of a certain group that can be used as an example of the rest of the group

Everyone hoped *Odyssey* would find and photograph a giant squid. Unfortunately, it never did.

In 1999, Dr. Roper and his team tried again. This time they used a submersible. Each day, a scientist used it to descend to the ocean floor. No one saw any giant squids.

How Do We Know About Giant Squids?

How do we know so much about these mysterious creatures if no one has ever seen one alive? That's easy. Every year, a few dead giant squids get caught in fishermen's nets and wash up on shores around the world. Additionally, a few are also discovered each year in the stomachs of sperm whales. These whales feed on giant squids. In fact, scientists often find telltale tentacle marks on sperm whales—from giant squids fighting to get free.

Dead specimens provide valuable information. Scientists have learned that giant squids eat fish and smaller squids and that they are invertebrates. Invertebrates don't have bones. Instead, a giant squid has a feather-shaped blade, called a gladius, throughout its body. This blade helps to support the huge animal.

Scientists like Dr. Roper are determined to learn more. Someday, he is sure, he will meet this magnificent animal.

Each square in the background grid represents 5 feet. Scientists believe a giant squid can grow as long as 75 feet. You can see how an average teen might look compared to a giant squid!

The Search For The
Giant Squid

Visualize

The author organized the information in this article in a particular way: Each section includes something that happened (effect) and reasons why it happened (cause).

This graphic organizer lists effects from "The Search for the Giant Squid." Look back through the article to find the causes that led to each effect.

Effects (what happens)

The giant squid is an interesting-looking animal because...

Scientists have never been able to observe a giant squid in its natural habitat because...

Scientists have a better chance of finding giant squids in their deep-sea homes because...

Scientists know what giant squids look like because...

Causes (reasons why)

its two eyes are the size of basketballs

The Search For The Giant Squid

Summarize

After you read an article, you may want to recall it or tell someone what it was about. Summarizing the article is an excellent way to pass along the information.

As briefly as possible, summarize "The Search for the Giant Squid." Start by using the causes and effects from your graphic organizer.

_____

_____

_____

_____

_____

> My summary will start with the name of the article, which also tells the topic—searching for giant squids. Then I'll tell why the giant squid is so interesting.

Determine What Is Important

This is another good strategy to use with nonfiction. Articles include lots of information. Authors want their readers to remember the big ideas. This means that readers need to know which are the main ideas and which are the details. Details help you get a better understanding of the main idea. They also help you remember it. While details may be very interesting, it's the main idea that authors really want you to remember.

One sentence in each pair below tells an important main idea. One sentence tells an interesting detail. Fill in the bubble beside the main-idea sentence in each pair.

(A) The giant squid is a huge, mysterious-looking animal.
(B) Its toothed tongue is called a radula.

(C) Dr. Roper, an expert on giant squids, has twice tried to find one.
(D) The *Odyssey*, used in his first expedition, weighs 430 pounds.

(E) Scientists have learned about giant squids by studying dead ones.
(F) A giant squid has a feather-shaped blade called a gladius.

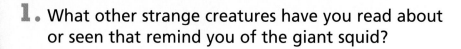

Make Connections

Think about the two selections you have just read. What do they remind you of? Connect them to other things you have read, to your experiences, and to the world around you.

1. What other strange creatures have you read about or seen that remind you of the giant squid?

_____

_____

2. How are these creatures like giant squids? How are they different?

_____

_____

3. How do you think Dr. Lopez felt when she finally observed the giant squid? Think of a time when you felt like that. Briefly tell about your experience.

_____

_____

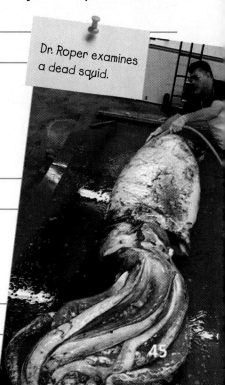

Dr. Roper examines a dead squid.

4. Dr. Lopez was a fictional scientist studying giant squids. How similar is her work to the work of Dr. Roper, a real-life scientist who studies giant squids?

_____

_____

5. How do both of these scientists remind you of other scientists you have read about?

_____

_____

45

Write A Descriptive Postcard

Write a postcard to a friend. Describe seeing a giant squid. Include details from both selections to help your friend picture this amazing animal.

BLACKLINE MASTER Before you write, use the Blackline Master your teacher will give you to plan your postcard.

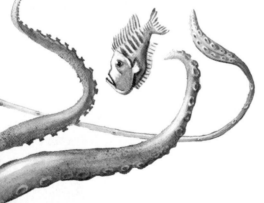

Plan Your Research

What else would you like to learn about giant squids or other deep-sea creatures? Write at least 3 questions you have about these creatures that you would like answered.

_____

_____

_____

_____

_____

_____

Net Connection

http://www.acsonline.org/factpack/spermwhl.htm
http://seawifs.gsfc.nasa.gov/squid.html

Another Dry Day

What would you do if you met someone from another place? What if that person was from another *time*? In this fantasy, a young girl meets the unexpected—and the unusual—during a drought of hot, dry weather.

Think About Genre

You already know that literature can be classified by genre, or type. This is a fantasy story. A fantasy story tells about events that might never happen in real life. The characters may not be realistic. Some fantasies combine events of the real and the unreal. For example, a person like you might meet an imaginary creature, such as a dragon. All the parts of a story—setting, characters, plot, problem, solution—are

included in a fantasy. What predictions can you make about "Another Dry Day"? Write *true* or *false* next to each statement.

1. _____ All the events in a fantasy could really happen.

2. _____ There is at least one event that is not realistic.

3. _____ Some of the characters may be imaginary and others may not.

4. _____ Fantasies are made-up stories.

Think About the Topic

Reread the introduction to "Another Dry Day." Fill in the bubble next to the word or phrase that best completes each statement.

1. A long period of hot, dry weather is called a _____
   - Ⓐ flood
   - Ⓒ drought
   - Ⓑ northeaster
   - Ⓓ hail storm

2. During a drought,_____
   - Ⓐ there is not enough water
   - Ⓑ plants grow well
   - Ⓒ rivers and lakes overflow
   - Ⓓ animals have plenty to drink

Think Ahead

Preview the story. Read the title, flip through the pages, and look at the illustrations before you read. This can help you predict what the story will be about. After previewing, write your prediction on the lines below.

_____

_____

_____

_____

_____

Another Dry Day

QUESTION
Ask yourself some questions about the setting of this story.

Where does this story take place? It sounds like a place I could go myself — a cabin in the woods with a lake nearby.

Is the setting of this story realistic? Why or why not?

drought (DROWT)
a long period of very dry weather

Stacey stepped out of the cabin, shutting the door softly behind her. No need to wake the others, she thought. She, Mom, Dad, and Brian had been together now for a whole week. Four people in the car, four people in the cabin. She really did need some time for herself.

Stacey started down the path to the lake. The sun was barely up, but she knew it would be another hot, dry day, just as it had been for weeks. They were calling it a **drought**.

Stacey came to the shore of the lake. Even if she had not known about the drought, the lake would have given it away. The water level was much lower than usual. You could almost wade to the floating dock. Last year only the really good swimmers could reach it.

Stacey shook her head. *I wonder how long the drought will last? And what will happen to the fish and the animals and the people who use the lake?* Feeling kind of down, she turned back toward the cabin and was surprised to see a girl about her age sitting on one of the logs that marked the edge of the path. She was staring at the lake. Somehow, though, she seemed to be far away.

The girl didn't even turn her head as Stacey came closer. How pale she was! She had a soft gray look about her, as if she had been ill for a long time. Even her clothes were gray. Whatever color they once were had long since faded away.

"Hi," said Stacey. The girl turned her head, though she did not look right at Stacey.

"I'm Stacey. My family's here from—" She did not get a chance to finish.

"I'm Rachel. We're headed for California, too."

"But—"

"We should have left before, before the dust storms got so bad."

"The dust storms?" asked Stacey, puzzled. Something was really strange. She hadn't heard about any dust storms lately. And she and her family were definitely not headed for California!

The girl kept talking, as if Stacey had not spoken.

"It got so bad, we couldn't even open the windows. The dust would get into everything. Mama even had to mix the food in a drawer to keep the dust from getting into it."

Stacey stared down at Rachel, saying nothing.

UNDERSTAND GENRE
(fantasy)

What clues does the author give you to suggest that there is something different, or even "unreal," about Rachel?

MAKE INFERENCES
What do you think Stacey is thinking when Rachel says her mother mixed food in a drawer to keep the dust out?

What can you infer about Rachel?

dust storm (DUHST storm) a storm with high winds that carry clouds of dust instead of rain

This Time Was Different

UNDERSTAND GENRE
(informational article)

For an informational article, change each heading into a question. You'll get an idea of what that part of the article tells you.

Why was it "no ordinary drought"?

Describe why this was no ordinary drought.

_____

_____

_____

_____

_____

recreation (rec-ree-AY-shun) play, such as boating, swimming, and fishing

No Ordinary Drought

This was no ordinary drought. There had been droughts before, and there would be more. But this time was different.

In normal times, there is enough rainfall to keep lakes and rivers at their usual levels. The lakes and streams are full of life. Deer and other animals drink the water. Bears come to look for fish. Human beings use the water for recreation. When there is normal rainfall, farmers grow their crops. They can feed and water their animals.

Sometimes, though, there is not enough rainfall. Then there is less water in the rivers and streams. There is not enough water for all the animals, and some die. Crops suffer, too. It may also be very hot, which makes matters even worse. These are signs of a serious drought, and it can last for years.

The Great Plains region of the United States has at times suffered from droughts. But none of them was as bad as the one that hit in the 1930s. The worst years were 1935 to 1938. During that time, there were many dust storms. In a dust storm, strong winds blow the dirt around. Anyone outdoors can easily get lost. It is hard to see even a few feet ahead. It is hard to breathe, too.

Black Sunday

Dirt from the sand storms piled up against barns and houses. It surrounded cars and farm machines, getting into the engines and ruining them. It swallowed up crops, leaving little if anything to harvest. It got into people's houses and anything that was not covered.

The Dust Bowl

Strong winds carried the soil across the Great Plains region of the United States: Texas, Oklahoma, Kansas, Colorado, Wyoming, Nebraska, South Dakota, and North Dakota.

MAKE CONNECTIONS

Make a connection between the information about Black Sunday with something else you have read.

I read about Black Sunday in "Another Dry Day," so I already have some idea of what happened then.

What facts in this article are similar to what Rachel described in "Another Dry Day"?

_____

_____

_____

_____

The worst time was what people called the black blizzard. Instead of snow, the winds carried dirt. Things did not start out badly that day. In fact, on this Sunday morning, it seemed like there was a break in the weather. It was hot, in fact the hottest day of the year so far. And it was clear, something that had not been true for months. Many people thought it was a good time to catch up on outdoor chores and activities, such as hanging out the laundry or just playing outside.

The dust-free break did not last long. Soon the sky turned black, and a choking dust storm struck. The churning cloud may have been as much as 7,000 feet high. People raced to get indoors. But nothing could stop the dust from getting into their houses. Soon everything was dirtied by the dust that easily blew through the cracks and onto dishes, food, and clothes.

When it was over, people had to shovel out what was left of their lives. It was this storm that earned the region the name the "Dust Bowl."

churning (CHUR-ning)
moving roughly

A line of trees may break the force of the wind.

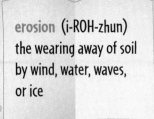

erosion (i-ROH-zhun)
the wearing away of soil by wind, water, waves, or ice

Can It Happen Again?

The Dust Bowl changed millions of people's lives. Many headed West to California to escape the drought and find a better life. The government of the United States tried to help those who were left. They taught people ways to protect the soil from **erosion**.

Erosion occurs when soil is loose enough for the wind to blow it away. One reason for the erosion was that there was nothing left to hold the soil. The region had once been grassland, and the grass kept the soil from blowing away. Then farmers came and planted wheat, which did not protect the soil as well as the grass did. Too many cattle meant that even more grassland was lost. Then the drought hit, making the dry soil even easier to blow away.

Scientists who understood good farming methods shared what they knew. For example, they said that planting lines of trees in certain places would break the force of the wind. The scientists also said that if farmers followed good soil and water conservation methods, there would never be another Dust Bowl.

Were they right? There have always been droughts. There are places in the United States that are going through a drought right now. Still, scientists say that if people follow good soil and water conservation methods, there should be no more Dust Bowl days.

We can only hope they are right.

This Time Was Different

Visualize

The author suggests that certain actions of human beings caused the last Dust Bowl. How, then, can we use this knowledge to keep it from happening again?

Develop a plan of action. Look back through "This Time Was Different" to find ideas for solving the problem. Think about the things that need to be done. Then tell what you think the results of these actions will be.

Problem

How can we prevent dust bowls from happening again?

Action

Expected Results

This Time Was Different

Summarize

Being able to summarize an article can help you recall what you read. Fill in the bubble next to the elements you would include in a summary of "This Time Was Different." You might find it helpful to look at the action plan on the previous page.

(A) what the word *recreation* means

(B) the title of the article

(C) a description of the worst drought during the 1930s

(D) things people can do to prevent another Dust Bowl

Nothing could stop the dust from getting into machinery, barns, and houses.

Determine What Is Important

The most important, or main, idea of an informational article can sometimes be found in its title. Below are some other possible titles for "This Time Was Different." Choose the one that best reflects the main idea of the article. Tell why you made that choice.

1. The Day the Sky Turned Black _____

_____

_____

2. Put a Stop to Dust Bowls! _____

_____

_____

3. Let the Sunshine Come! _____

_____

_____

Make Connections

Even though "Another Dry Day" is a fantasy, it describes a real event—Black Sunday and the Dust Bowl. Connections to real events can make stories more interesting.

Another Dry Day

This Time Was Different

1. Write one more real event you have read about in a work of fiction.

_____

_____

_____

Many families made their way to California in the 1930s, looking for a better life.

2. Did the use of real events in the plot make the story more or less interesting? How or why?

_____

_____

_____

3. Stacey and Rachel are fictional characters. What kind of warning might a real Rachel have given Stacey about what could happen to her family?

_____

_____

_____

4. These selections refer to Black Sunday, a day of horrible weather through which people had to struggle. What other terrible weather event have you read about (in your science or social studies books) or heard about (in the news)? How is this event like Black Sunday? How is it different?

_____

_____

Write a Diary Entry

Imagine that Rachel from "Another Dry Day" kept a diary. What would she have written about Black Sunday? Think about what you learned about that day in "Another Dry Day" and "This Time Was Different" in your diary entry. Remember to use descriptive words and details in your writing.

Dear Diary

_____

_____

_____

_____

_____

BLACKLINE MASTER Before you write, use the Blackline Master your teacher will give you to plan your diary entry.

Plan your Research

There are important ways all of us can help to conserve natural resources such as water, soil, and energy. Select one natural resource. What would you like to learn about it? Write three questions you would like to have answered through your research.

1. _____

_____

2. _____

_____

3. _____

_____

Net Connection

http://www.discovery.com/area/history/dustbowl/dustbowlopener.html

Getting Ready

Fires of Pele

Watch out! Pele (PAY-lay) is about to go into another rage! When Pele loses her temper, the earth itself begins to tremble, and red-hot lava flows over the land. In this Hawaiian myth, discover how Pele came to Hawaii, and how she changed the land with her fury.

Think About Genre

One important type of fiction is the myth (MITH). Ancient people used myths to explain how and why things happened (similar to the *pourquoi* tale you learned about when you read "Out of the Light, Into the Night"). This was especially true when people of long ago tried to explain events they witnessed in nature. "Fires of Pele" is a Hawaiian myth that explains one kind of natural occurrence. What questions can you expect it to answer? Fill in the bubbles next to your choices. There may be more than one.

Ⓐ What does the myth explain?

Ⓑ How did the natural occurrences come to be?

Ⓒ Who or what caused it to happen?

Ⓓ Why did Hawaiians tell a myth about Pele?

Think About the Topic

What do you know about volcanoes? Reread the above introduction to "Fires of Pele." Write two facts about volcanoes below.

1._____

_____

2._____

_____

Think Ahead

Preview the myth. Think about the title, the map, and the illustrations. Which of the following is a good prediction of what you are about to read? Fill in the bubble.

Ⓐ The myth will tell how many times lava has flowed over the land.

Ⓑ The myth will explain why Hawaii has such good surfing.

Ⓒ The myth will tell why Hawaii has volcanoes.

Ⓓ The myth is about Honolulu.

Strategies:

UNDERSTAND GENRE
MAKE INFERENCES
VISUALIZE
QUESTION

Fires of Pele

UNDERSTAND GENRE
(myth)

As you read, ask yourself what forces of nature are being discussed.

> I read that Pele is the goddess of fire and volcanoes.

What clues help connect Pele to natural events?

_____

_____

_____

_____

_____

fiery (FY-ree) full of fire

temper (TEM-pur) personality, especially whether someone angers easily

volcanoes (vahl-KAY-noz) mountains from which hot, melted rock, ash, and gas erupt

A time long ago, in a faraway land known as Kahiki, there lived a mother, father, seven brothers, and seven sisters—all gods and goddesses.

One of the daughters was named Pele. Pele was the goddess of fire and volcanoes.

Pele had a terrible temper. Whenever she became angry or jealous, she would fly into a wild rage. If she stamped her feet in anger, the ground would shake. When she screamed, cried, or tossed her hair, fiery lava would flow down the mountainsides or shoot high up into the air.

Pele usually didn't stop to think about whether something was good or bad. She just did whatever she felt like doing at that moment. This often led to big trouble. For instance, there was the time she fell in love with the man her sister loved. Unfortunately, Na-maka-o-kaha'i, her sister, became very jealous and angry at Pele and set out to chase her away.

Pele quickly packed her things into a canoe and escaped from Kahiki. She traveled for a long time, far across the bright, warm Pacific Ocean.

At last, exhausted, Pele reached Kauai, where she rested awhile before climbing a mountain. When she reached the top, she carefully carved out a pit with her digging stick. She prepared to move into the pit and make it her home.

Pele's sister, Na-maka-o-kaha'i, had other plans. She was a goddess herself, of course—the goddess of seas and oceans. She had followed Pele all the way to the island and waited patiently until Pele had finished digging the pit in the mountaintop. Then, with her power, she caused the ocean waves to splash higher and higher until the pit disappeared under a pool of water. Pele was not discouraged though; she knew she had to move on and try again.

Pele landed next at the island of Oahu and dug a pit in the mountaintop there. However, her angry sister followed her and flooded that pit as well. Pele canoed from island to island—Molokai, Lanai and Maui. At each island she would climb a mountain, dig a pit, and prepare to move in. Then, Na-maka-o-kaha'i would splash the ocean waves higher and higher until the pit was flooded.

MAKE INFERENCES
Pele digs a hole in a mountaintop on each island, and each time, her sister floods it. What inferences can you make about the sisters' personalities?

digging stick (DIG-ing STIK) long, pointed stick used to make holes in the ground for planting seeds

VISUALIZE

Fiction writing often uses describing words. This helps you make a picture in your mind. Copy the phrases that help you visualize Pele.

QUESTION

Asking yourself questions can help you better understand a story.

What kinds of natural processes have been taking place in Hawaii since ancient times? Why might it be necessary to explain these processes with a myth?

Write two questions you might ask yourself as you read about long-ago Hawaii.

1.

2.

Finally, Pele landed on the "Big Island" of Hawaii. She climbed the mountain known as Mauna Loa. At the top of the mountain, she took her digging stick and carved out a huge pit. This time, she made sure she was very distant from the ocean waves. Na-maka-o-kaha'i splashed the waves as high as she could, but she couldn't splash them high enough to reach Pele and flood the pit.

Pele settled into Mauna Loa and there she stayed. But just as before, when she would lose her temper and fly into a rage, stamp her feet, scream, cry, and toss her hair the ground would shake and rumble. Hot lava would erupt into the air and flow down the mountainsides.

That is how the Hawaiian Islands came to be the way they are today. If you visit the islands of Hawaii you will find the huge craters, still filled with water. And if you visit Mauna Loa on the Big Island, you will feel the rumble, hear the roar, and see the lava flow and know that Pele has lost her temper.

craters (KRA tur)
pits or holes

distant (DIS-tint)
far away

Fires of Pele

Visualize

Look back in "Fires of Pele" to see what Pele did throughout the story. Think about how the author describes Pele. Make some inferences by using story clues to decide what Pele was like. Remember that a character may be different at different parts of the story.

I will think of what I know about Pele's actions, and about what a volcano does, to help me understand Pele's character traits.

A. How would you describe Pele's personality?

	How can you tell?
hot-tempered	She often gets angry.
independent	She sets off by herself on the ocean.

B. How does Pele feel when she is running away from her sister?

How can you tell?

C. How does Pele feel when her sister floods the first pit?

How can you tell?

D. How does Pele feel when she makes lava erupt and the ground shake?

How can you tell?

Fires of Pele

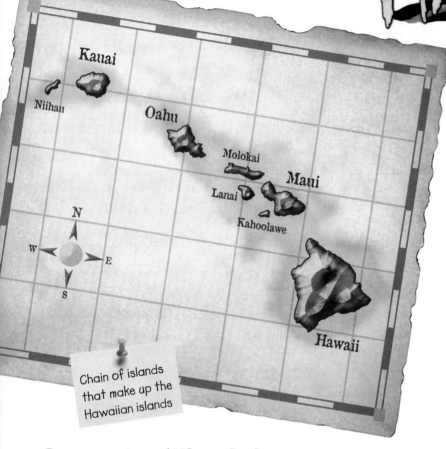

Chain of islands that make up the Hawaiian islands

Summarize

Once you have read a myth, you may want to think about the interesting way it explains a natural event. One way to do this is to summarize the story, or retell it briefly.

Fill in the bubble next to two things you might include in a summary of "Fires of Pele."

(A) real events

(B) the natural event the myth is explaining

(C) the definition of *digging stick*

(D) character, setting, plot

Determine What Is Important

When you read a selection, it is important to find the main ideas and connect them to what you already know. This helps you understand and remember new information.

1. List two things you already knew about Hawaii that helped you understand "Fires of Pele."

_____

_____

2. What main ideas from "Fires of Pele" did you connect to the two things you already knew about Hawaii?

_____

_____

Getting Ready

Mauna Loa is the tallest mountain on earth and one of the most active volcanoes. It is also a place of great mystery. Ancient Hawaiians believed that it was inhabited by Pele, goddess of fires and volcanoes. What is it about Mauna Loa that makes it so fascinating?

MAUNA LOA: LONG MOUNTAIN

Think About Genre

Fiction, such as a myth, tells a story. Nonfiction, like this article, tells you facts about a topic. As you read an informational article, you should watch for certain features. There may be headings within the article. The illustrations, maps, diagrams, and graphic aids may also provide additional information. Look at the article, "Mauna Loa: Long Mountain." Which features do you see? Write them on the lines below.

_____

_____

_____

_____

_____

_____

_____

_____

_____

Think About the Topic

Read the above introduction to the selection, "Mauna Loa: Long Mountain." Ask yourself, *What have I learned about Mauna Loa from reading "Fires of Pele"?* List two things that you learned.

1._____

_____

2._____

_____

Think Ahead

Take another quick look at the article. Think about the title and the features. Complete the sentences below.

1. I predict that I will learn _____

_____

_____

2. The photos and captions _____

_____

_____

Scientists have studied Mauna Loa and the Hawaiian Islands. They have discovered that the Hawaiian Islands are not all the same age. The most western island, Kauai, is the oldest. From west to east, each island is younger than the one before it.

Why did this happen? It wasn't by chance. There are a few underground zones on earth where molten rock is always very close to the surface. These zones are called "hot spots." There is a "hot spot" at the eastern end of the Hawaiian Islands. Right over it is Hawaii, the youngest island. There, Mauna Loa and the other active volcanoes are found. Volcanoes on the other, older islands are extinct.

The ancient Hawaiian myth about Pele, the volcano goddess, is like the scientific explanation in some important ways. In the myth, Pele arrived first at Kauai and dug a crater there, which her sister filled with sea water. This happened again and again as Pele traveled eastward from island to island. Finally, Pele settled in the crater of Mauna Loa. Whenever the hot-tempered Pele got upset, she caused lava to flow and the ground to shake. In fact, Mauna Loa is an active volcano. Pele's earlier "homes" are actually extinct volcanoes.

How Do People Feel About Mauna Loa?

Throughout time, the people who have lived in the shadow of Mauna Loa have wondered why the volcano erupts and how to protect themselves. In Hawaii, Mauna Loa will remain a "hot topic" for generations to come.

MAKE CONNECTIONS

The scientific information about the Hawaiian Islands is similar to the events in the myth about Pele.

Yes, I remember that Pele visited the islands in a particular order. It looks like that order has something to do with the age of each island.

What is one other fact about the volcanoes you can infer by reading the myth of Pele?

_____

_____

_____

_____

_____

extinct (ek-STINKT) no longer active

SIGNS OF PELE

Hawaiians still feel a strong connection to the Pele myth. One sign of this is the name of some lava formations.

Pele's tears, a lava formation, occurs when bits of lava cool and harden in midair.

This stringy, glassy lava formation is called Pele's hair.

Visualize

The overall main idea of the article is about Mauna Loa. The information in each section is used to support the overall main idea. Each section includes its own main idea and details. Look back through each section of the article to find details that support the overall main idea. Write them on the lines below.

I will use the central idea behind the article for my main idea. Then I will look for details that support the main idea.

Main Idea

Mauna Loa is a huge volcano in Hawaii.

Detail	Detail	Detail	Detail	Detail

Summarize

Information in an article may catch
your interest and cause you to want
to find out more. To decide what else you want to learn, organize your thoughts into
a summary of things you already know.

As briefly as possible, summarize "Mauna Loa: Long Mountain." Include some of
the details from your graphic organizer.

_____

_____

_____

_____

Determine What Is Important

Not every fact in an article is necessary to a summary of it. You need to decide which
are the most important and include one or two details that support each main idea.

Read each pair of sentences. Decide which one tells a main idea and which one
gives a detail. Fill in the bubble next to the main idea.

Ⓐ Today, Mauna Loa is part of Hawaii Volcanoes National Park.
Ⓑ Hikers have to check in with park rangers before they go out on a trail.

Ⓒ The youngest island is Hawaii.
Ⓓ Hawaii's islands are formed in line from the oldest to the youngest.

Ⓔ Mauna Loa's base is below sea level on the ocean floor.
Ⓕ Mauna Loa is taller than Mount Everest.

Ⓖ Mauna Loa has erupted at least 30 times in the past 160 years.
Ⓗ Mauna Loa is one of the most active volcanoes on earth.

Make Connections

Think about the two selections you have read. How can you
tie this new information to things that you already know
about nature and volcanoes? Connect what you have read
to your experiences, to things you know about nature in general
and volcanoes in particular, and to the world around you.

1. Why might living near an active volcano cause ancient Hawaiians to think it
was created by a character like Pele, goddess of volcanoes?

_____

_____

_____

2. What other myths or fables do you know that explain how something works
in the world?

_____

_____

_____

3. In the myth, Pele's anger caused volcanic eruptions. When people you
know get angry, what does their anger cause to happen?

_____

_____

_____

4. What landforms (such as mountains, beaches, lakes) are your favorites? Why?

_____

_____

_____

Write a Descriptive Paragraph

Imagine that you have just visited Mauna Loa at Hawaii Volcanoes National Park. Write a paragraph that tells about your experience. Use descriptive words to explain the mountain's features and to relate your feelings. Think about what you read in "Fires of Pele" and "Mauna Loa: Long Mountain" to help you.

_____

_____

_____

_____

_____

BLACKLINE MASTER Before you write, use the Blackline Master your teacher will give you to plan your paragraph.

Black lava coastline and Mauna Loa volcano

Plan Your Research

Think of what you have learned about volcanoes. What else would you like to know? Brainstorm a list of 5 questions about volcanoes that you would like to have answered in your research.

What you **K**now	What you **W**ould like to know
	1.
	2.
	3.
	4.
	5.

Net Connection

http://www.hawaii-forest.com/essays/9712.html

That MAN from WASHINGTON

A stagecoach thunders into a small western town where two boys live.
Who's inside? It is that man from Washington—the president of the United States!

Think About Genre

Historical fiction is a type of fiction. It quickly sets the story in a time and place of the past. The author uses real events, places, and people from history. However, since the story is fiction, some of the events, people, and conversations are made up.

Read each statement below. Circle **T** if you think the statement about historical fiction is true, or **F** if you think the statement is false.

1. When you read historical fiction, you can expect the setting to always be in the near or distant past.

    T   **F**

2. All of the characters in a historical fiction story actually lived.

    T   **F**

Think About the Topic

Reread the introduction to "That Man from Washington." Ask yourself *What clues give me an idea of what this story is going to be about?* Then complete the following sentence:

    I can tell that a real person will be

_____

_____

_____

Think Ahead

Reread the introduction. Preview the story by looking at the illustrations. Fill in the bubble next to the best prediction of what the story will be about.

Ⓐ It will be about Washington, D.C.

Ⓑ It will be about Washington State.

Ⓒ It will be about two boys.

Ⓓ It will be about parks.

Reading Fiction

Strategies:

QUESTION
UNDERSTAND GENRE
VISUALIZE
MAKE CONNECTIONS

QUESTION

Ask questions as you read. For example, *What* is happening as the story opens?

Write a *Who* question about this part of the story on the lines below. Circle the answer when you find it in the story.

bedpost (BED-pohst) a vertical post, or support, at the corner of a bed

hurling (HUR-ling) throwing or tossing

That MAN from WASHINGTON

The giant bear held David by his shoulders and shook him so hard that his blanket fell off. David grabbed his attacker, but he could not hold on. Another minute and he would be in the campfire.

"Open your eyes, lazy bones. Get up or you'll miss the whole show!"

David opened his eyes. Sunlight was pouring into the attic room where he and his older brother slept above their father's store. His blanket was twisted around him, making it difficult to avoid the clothes Josh was **hurling** at him.

David was able to grab his socks and shirt and unwind his pants from the **bedpost**. He dressed quickly and rushed to catch up with Josh. He still did not know what "the whole show" was. All he knew was that he was not going to miss it, whatever "it" was.

"What's going on?" he finally managed to ask.

"He's downstairs," Josh said in a loud whisper. "That man from Washington! But he's not going to be here for long! So get moving."

It finally sank in. All he had heard for the past week, the dream he had last night of camping in Yosemite (yo-SEH-mih-tee), that man from Washington—everything finally came together.

It was all anyone had talked about for days. That man from Washington—the president of the United States, Teddy Roosevelt (ROH-zuh-velt)—was coming to their part of the country. He was going to be camping in Yosemite with the great naturalist John Muir (MYOOR). Muir had often stopped in Clarkson's General Store to get supplies.

The boys' best hope was that they might get a glimpse of the president as his stagecoach passed near the edge of town on its way to Yosemite. But now Josh was saying that the president was actually in the store!

The boys tumbled down the stairs and looked around the dimily-lit room. It took a moment for them to get used to the light. When they did, they saw their father's familiar figure by the window with his head bent over another man's hand.

He had just finished bandaging the man's hand and was saying, "There, that should be better now. Just keep it clean."

The man—it was not the president—thanked him, then turned to someone speaking from the shadows. As he spoke, Josh poked David in the arm.

"That's him!" squealed Josh.

They watched as an arm reached out from the darkness and shook Mr. Clarkson's hand. Then the figure turned and walked outside.

UNDERSTAND GENRE
(historical fiction)

The author gives clues that tell you this story takes place in the past. On the lines below, list one.

VISUALIZE
Picture the person standing in the shadows. Describe what you see.

Josh says "That's him!" I think that he's talking about the president. I'll imagine what Teddy Roosevelt looks like from pictures I have seen of him.

general store (JEN-ur-uhl STOR) a small store that sells different kinds of goods

naturalist (NAH-chur-ah-list) one who studies plants and animals in their natural habitats, or homes

"Boys, come over here," Mr. Clarkson called.

When they went to their father, Mr. Clarkson introduced the man whose hand he had bandaged. He was a photographer and part of the president's party. He would be taking pictures of the president and Mr. Muir as they traveled around together.

"What happened to your hand, sir?" David asked. He was hoping to hear a story about how the man had hurt it defending the president's life. Instead, the man smiled rather foolishly.

Looking down at his bandaged hand, the man answered. "The extra **lens** for my camera broke in my pack. I didn't know that, so when I reached in to get something, I cut myself." He turned to Mr. Clarkson. "Your father was kind enough to help me bandage my hand. Now I need to pay him."

Mr. Clarkson shook his head and waved his hand to say no. "It's as much as I'd do for anyone. Having the chance to meet President Roosevelt—well, there's no price on that!"

All four walked to the door of the store together. They watched as the president and his party got back on the stagecoach. The coach had made a special stop at Clarkson's General Store to get help for the photographer. Now the stagecoach driver had to **make up the time**. Only a few minutes had passed. But David knew that he and his brother would remember them always.

MAKE CONNECTIONS
As you read, try to make connections between story events and your own life. Mr. Clarkson says, "Having the chance to meet President Roosevelt!"
Maybe you have met someone you will never forget. Briefly tell about that meeting.

---

lens (lenz) a curved piece of glass used in cameras

make up the time an expression that means "to go or travel quickly"

Visualize

That MAN from WASHINGTON

Think about the sequence, or order, of events
that brought Theodore Roosevelt to David's town.
The order may be different from the way you read about it in the story.

Use the time line to list the important events in the order in which you think they happened.

When you finish your time line, circle the one event that is the turning point of the story. That is, the whole story would have been different if this event had not happened.

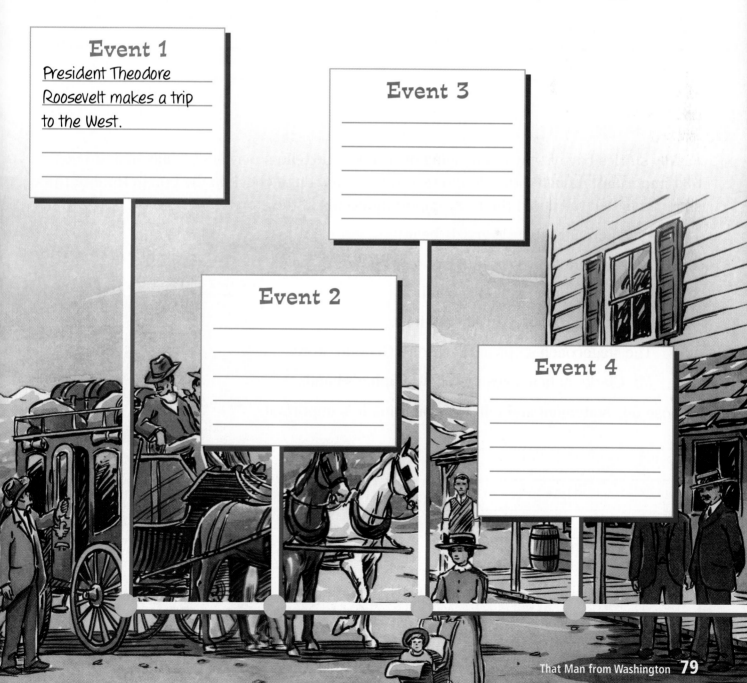

Event 1
President Theodore
Roosevelt makes a trip
to the West.

Event 3

Event 2

Event 4

Summarize

Imagine that David is all grown up, telling his own children about the time the president of the United States stopped at his family's store.

*That **MAN** from* **WASHINGTON**

Write your version of the story he will tell about "That Man from Washington." You may want to look at your time line for ideas.

_____

_____

_____

_____

_____

Determine What Is Important

Family stories have a way of changing over time. The tellers may add details that are not that important, though they add interest to the story. Put a check in the box in front of three statements that tell about the most important events in the story.

1. ☐ David dreams about a grizzly bear.

2. ☐ President Roosevelt makes a trip to the West.

3. ☐ The photographer cuts his hand.

4. ☐ The photographer has an extra lens.

5. ☐ The stagecoach stops at Clarkson's General Store.

6. ☐ Mr. Clarkson bandages the photographer's hand.

Choose one statement and tell why you think it is important.

_____

_____

Getting Ready

It is hard to sum up the life of a great man, never mind *two* men, who changed the direction of the country. Would these men have chosen the same events their biographer did to tell about their lives?

A MEETING OF MINDS

Think About Genre

Biographical sketches are short descriptions of real events in people's lives. They include facts about important things that the person did. The settings and characters are real.

Fill in the bubble beside the three features you can expect to find in "A Meeting of Minds."

(A) real settings

(B) made-up characters

(C) facts

(D) real people

Think About the Topic

Read the introduction to "A Meeting of Minds." Think about two "real people" in "That Man from Washington." What do you think they were doing out west?

_____

_____

_____

Think Ahead

Preview the biographical sketch, "A Meeting of Minds." Predict why these two men came together. In what way might they have had "A Meeting of Minds" or, an agreement about something?

_____

_____

_____

_____

_____

A MEETING OF MINDS

Two important men pose at Glacier Point in Yosemite, May 1903.

MAKE INFERENCES

From what you have read, explain why you think John Muir earned the honor of being known as "a voice for the wilderness."

_____

_____

_____

_____

wilderness
(WIL-dur-nes) a wild place with no people living in it

It is just an old black-and-white photograph of two men, yet it is so much more. It is a reminder of an event that occurred many years ago. And the effects of that event still continue to be felt, even today, because of this meeting between the two great men in the photograph—Theodore "Teddy" Roosevelt, president of the United States, and John Muir, explorer, naturalist, and writer. What they did—together and on their own—changed the United States forever.

JOHN MUIR: VOICE OF THE WILDERNESS

John Muir was born in Scotland on April 21, 1838. When he was 11 years old, his family came to the United States. Life on a Wisconsin farm led to Muir's great love of nature.

In the spring of 1869, Muir decided to travel through California. It turned out to be a turning point in his life. Muir explored the Sierra (see-EH-ruh) Nevada, a mountain range in eastern California. The state was to become his life-long home.

For six years he lived in the Yosemite Valley and studied its forests and rock formations. In 1892, Muir founded the Sierra Club, which works to protect wilderness areas. Muir also wrote a number of books with the same goal in mind. By speaking and writing, Muir was able to "speak" for the wilderness and wildlife, giving them their own "voice." He became known in the United States and around the world as "the voice of the wilderness."

1838 John Muir [JM] is born.	1858 Theodore Roosevelt [TR] is born.	1890 JM influences the establishment of Yosemite and Sequoia National Parks.	1892 JM founds the Sierra Club.	1901 SEPTEMBER Vice president TR becomes president when William McKinley is killed.	1901 DECEMBER TR tells Congress that the country must preserve its forests.	1903 JM and TR camp together in Yosemite.	1904 TR is elected president.	1906 Yosemite Valley and the Groves become parts of the National Park System.

Each date on this time line marks an important point in increasing the country's understanding of the need for preservation.

THEODORE ROOSEVELT: PRESERVATION PRESIDENT

As a man, Theodore Roosevelt was always full of energy, whether at work or play. He loved to read, and he enjoyed almost any outdoor activity. As a boy, he had shown an early interest in nature. But Roosevelt had not been a strong child, and he was often sick.

Then one year, when he was about 12 years old, he was bullied by two other boys. Roosevelt was upset that he was not strong enough to fight back. To help him, his father built a gym right in their family home. The future president built up his strength by exercising in the gym.

Roosevelt became president in 1901. Most Americans called him Teddy or simply T.R. As president, Roosevelt was interested in reform, or change—he wanted to make things better for Americans. One reform he supported was conserving, or saving, the country's forests. In his first message to Congress, Roosevelt made it clear that the **preservation** of forests was very important to him.

Roosevelt decided to talk to as many **experts** on the subject as possible so that he could learn more from them. Not surprisingly, one of those experts was the naturalist John Muir.

After a cartoon showed President Roosevelt with a bear cub, toy makers started making stuffed animals they called "teddy" bears after T.R.

UNDERSTAND GENRE
(biographical sketch)

How do you think a biographer might have learned that Roosevelt was upset about being bullied?

_____

_____

_____

expert (EK-spurt) a person who knows a lot about something

preservation (preh-zur-VAY-shun) keeping safe

That **MAN** *from*
WASHINGTON

**A MEETING
OF MINDS**

Write a Speech

John Muir Day in California is April 21, Muir's birthday.
Think of what you would like to tell people about John Muir.
Write a speech that you could present to your classmates.

_____

_____

_____

_____

_____

_____

**BLACKLINE
MASTER** Before you write, use the Blackline Master your
teacher will give you to plan your speech.

Plan Your Research

What else would you like to know about the lives of Theodore Roosevelt and
John Muir? What are some good search words you could use in the library or
on the Internet? Write them below along with your questions.

Search Words	Questions

*Net
Connection*

http://sierraclub.org/john_muir_exhibit/

Getting Ready

CELEBRITY MICROBES

It's Science Week at Lake Vista Elementary School. Raoul Velez has written a class play on this year's theme—"Life All Around Us." Take a sneak peek at dress rehearsal. Discover some of the fascinating facts about microbes—tiny living things—that Raoul wants to share with you.

Think About Genre

Plays are one of the oldest genres in literature. In a play, the story is written to be performed. There are no quotation marks around the dialogue, instead a character's name appears first, set off by a colon. Then, the words that the character speaks, follow.

The script includes the character's feelings and some of the character's actions.

"Celebrity Microbes" is a fictional play. Fill in the circle of the statements below that you think will be true as you read "Celebrity Microbes":

(A) It will have a setting, plot, and characters.

(B) It will have a lot of description.

(C) The dialogue will be spoken out loud.

(D) It will have action.

Think About the Topic

Read the introduction to "Celebrity Microbes." Ask yourself the following questions. They will help you think about the topic. Write your answers on the lines.

1. In what form of literature is this story written?_____

2. What living things does Raoul write about?_____
   _____

3. What do you know about germs?_____
   _____

Think Ahead

Take another look at "Celebrity Microbes." Reread the introduction. Then circle the sentence that you think tells what the play will be about.

1. Famous people are getting awards.

2. Some microbes are well-known.

3. Microbes help people's lives in many ways.

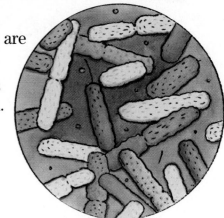

Strategies:
UNDERSTAND GENRE
VISUALIZE
MAKE CONNECTIONS

CELEBRITY MICROBES

UNDERSTAND GENRE
Think of the features of a play. List two features that help you get some idea of the story.

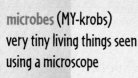

microbes (MY-krobs)
very tiny living things seen using a microscope

Cast of Characters

Dr. Petrie Dish (PE-tree dish)
Assistant

The AWARD Nominees:
E. Coli (EE KOH-lie)
Acidophilus (A-si-DAH-fih-lus)
Yeast (YEEST)
Methanotroph (meh-than-uh-TROF)
Oil-eater
Antibiotic

(The scene opens on stage at a ceremony modeled after the Academy Awards. The characters are all dressed very formally.)

DR. PETRIE DISH: Hello, friends! Welcome to the First Annual International Celebrity **Microbes** Awards! Our goal tonight is to celebrate some little-known facts about microbes. Since microbes were discovered about four centuries ago, the very word has struck fear into people's hearts. We knew microbes only as the cause of some of the deadliest diseases on earth. Microbes, we discovered, were to blame for such horrible diseases as the bubonic plague, tuberculosis, and malaria, to name just a few. However, not all microbes are bad. What about the world's helpful and even heroic microbes? In honor of these hardworking, unsung life forms, we dedicate these awards.

(Applause)

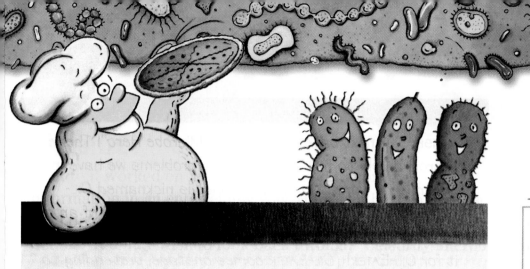

DR. DISH: Our first award category is "Best Everyday Microbe." The first nominee is YEAST. Without YEAST, we'd have no bread, rolls, or pizza. You are the fungus that causes dough to rise. Come on up, YEAST, rise and take a bow. *(YEAST, in a baker's hat, joins DR. DISH on stage.)* Next is ACIDOPHILUS, which can turn milk to yogurt and cheese. Right up here, ACIDOPHILUS! *(ACIDOPHILUS, leading a cow, comes on stage and waves to the audience.)* Finally, where would we be without E. COLI? This microbe works to keep our **digestive systems** healthy. Folks, I think E. COLI is too shy to join us. However, E. COLI is indeed a nominee. The envelope, please. *(An Assistant hands a large envelope to DR. DISH.)*

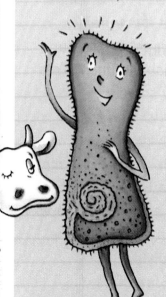

DR. DISH *(opens envelope dramatically):* And the winner is . . . E. COLI! Let's give a big hand to E. COLI for the wonderful job it performs in our bodies every single day! *(DR. DISH holds up a trophy.)* We'll get this to E. after the show. Thank you all! *(YEAST and ACIDOPHILUS walk offstage waving to the crowd, as audience applauds.)*

VISUALIZE

The author includes notes in the text of a play that tell the actors what to do. These are called "stage directions." The stage directions for "Celebrity Microbes" are in parentheses.

> How do the stage directions help me picture what is happening?

Describe what you see happening.

_____

_____

_____

digestive system (dih-JES-tiv SIS-tim) the organs and passages in the body used to eat and process food

MICROBES

Influenced (IN-floo-enst) caused a change

rebellion (rih-BEL-yin) uprising against a government

vaccine (vak-SEEN) drug that prevents a person from catching a particular disease

Microbes in History

Microbes live in us, on us, and around us. They can feed us; they can starve us. So it should come as no surprise that these tiny creatures have **influenced** human history in countless ways.

Mosquitoes carrying the yellow fever virus helped the cause of freedom in Haiti. In 1791, French Emperor Napoleon Bonaparte sent 33,000 soldiers to put down a **rebellion** led by a former African slave, Toussaint-L'Ouverture (above). Within months, yellow fever had nearly wiped out the French troops. The loss helped persuade Napoleon to grant the French colony its independence.

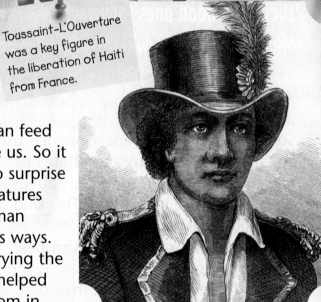
Toussaint-L'Ouverture was a key figure in the liberation of Haiti from France.

Microbe Detectives Through the Ages...

1796 Edward Jenner invents a smallpox **vaccine** using a milder microbe called cowpox. By the late 1900s, smallpox is all but eliminated in the world.

1860 Louis Pasteur proves the "germ theory of disease," stating that every infectious disease is caused by a specific microbe.

Ship with linen sails made from flax

Two little soil microbes, *Clostridium felsineum* and *Clostridium pectinovorum*, helped launch the spread of human civilization. These two bacteria are responsible for the growing of the flax plant and for preparing flax fibers for weaving linen. Linen was used to make the sailcloth that powered the ships.

A disease-causing microbe also helped write the history of medieval Europe. The microbe arrived on flea-infested rats living aboard a trading ship returning from Asia. Europe was overpopulated and filthy—ideal conditions for an **epidemic**. Within four years, a disease known as the bubonic plague, or Black Death, had claimed 25 million lives, or about one-third of all Europe.

Flea-infested rat, carrier of the bubonic plague

MAKE INFERENCES

What inference can you draw about what microbes had to do with spreading civilization, as it says in the article? Fill in the bubble next to the best answer and explain.

Ⓐ Microbes were used in the making of linen cloth.

Ⓑ Linen was used in making sails for ships and the ship's travel spread civilization.

Ⓒ Microbes caused people to want to share knowledge.

_____

_____

_____

_____

1928 Alexander Fleming discovers that a mold called *Penicillum* kills bacteria, paving the way for the use of antibiotics.

1955 Jonas Salk develops a **vaccine** against polio using killed polio viruses. Today, the crippling disease is nearly wiped out in the United States.

epidemic (eh-pi-DEH-mik) outbreak of disease affecting many people

Summarize

The format of "Microbes" is different from an article that is mostly text. It presents a lot of different kinds of information. Also, it uses a lot more art. Still, you can summarize material that is presented this way.
  Read each summary. Fill in the circle in front of the best summary.

Ⓐ Microbes are good and bad. Microbes are tiny. Scientists study microbes. Microbes have affected human civilization.

Ⓑ Microbes are tiny living things. Microbes cause disease. Microbes treat the human body like an ecosystem. Malaria-causing microbes led to the independence of Haiti. Edward Jenner invented the smallpox vaccine. By the late 1900s, smallpox was basically wiped out. Polio is also caused by microbes.

Ⓒ Microbes are tiny living things. They are both helpful and harmful. Life as we know it would not be possible without these little organisms. Scientists have discovered that some microbes cause disease. Microbes have affected many parts of human life, for good and for bad

Determine What Is Important

As you think back over "Microbes," what information was most important to you? Use the chart below. Write what was important to you in the left column. Write why it was important in the middle column. Write whether it was a main idea or a detail in the right column. A sample chart appears below.

Important Item	Why Is This Important?	Main Idea or Detail?

CELEBRITY MICROBES

MICROBES

Make Connections

Think about "Celebrity Microbes" and "Microbes."
Then complete the activities.

1. Which big idea could apply to both selections? Fill in the circle next to it.

Ⓐ Microbes should get awards for the good things they do, but not for the bad.

Ⓑ There is no need to do any more research on microbes, for much has been done already.

Ⓒ Microbes have played a very large role in human life, including health, culture, and history.

2. Using information from both selections, list one piece of information about microbes that was the most surprising to you.

_____

_____

3. After reading about microbes and health, how likely is it that you will change what you do or how you live? Circle your answer, and explain your choice.

Very likely   **Somewhat likely**   **Not likely**

_____

_____

4. Add to Raoul Velez's play. Look back at the timeline, "Microbe Detectives Through the Ages." Write a sentence that one of the scientists might say about his work.

_____

_____

Putting Fiction And Nonfiction Together

CELEBRITY MICROBES

MICROBES

Make a Sequel

The play "Celebrity Microbes" was such a success that people are calling for a sequel. Work alone or with a partner to write another play, based on the information in "Microbes." Use the lines below to make some notes on what to include.

_____

_____

_____

_____

BLACKLINE MASTER Before you write, use the Blackline Master your teacher will give you to plan your sequel.

Plan Your Research

As you think back over the new facts you read in these selections, which ones would you like to know more about? Use an idea web like the one to the right to come up with some new questions. Write the main topic in the center, and the ideas or questions in the bubbles. Use the timeline in "Microbes" to write some of your questions.

Net Connection
http://www.microbe.org/

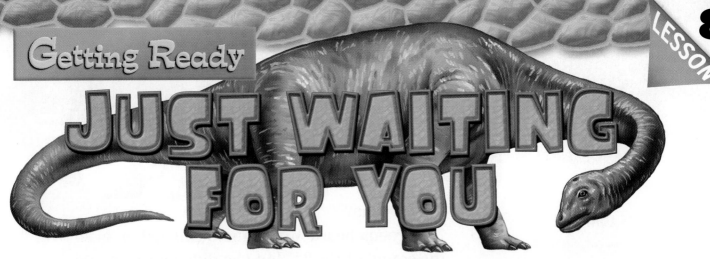

Getting Ready
JUST WAITING FOR YOU

Dinosaurs! Many people, young and old, are fascinated by these enormous creatures that once ruled the earth. Will Coreena fall under their spell?

Think About Genre

In realistic fiction, the events described could really happen. Settings are realistic, too. The characters are the kinds of people you might meet in real life, and they have problems that sound familiar to you.

What can you expect from this kind of fiction? Complete the sentence below.

This story will feature characters

who _____

and whose problems _____

Think About the Topic

If you watch TV or see movies, you have probably seen animated dinosaurs. Compare and contrast what they are like with what you know about real dinosaurs.

Animated Dinosaurs	Real Dinosaurs

Think Ahead

Preview the story by taking a quick look at the title and illustrations. Fill in the bubble next to the best prediction of what the story will tell about.

(A) The story will tell about someone who is interested in dinosaurs.

(B) The story will tell about making a cartoon about dinosaurs.

(C) The story will tell about the dangers of watching too much television.

(D) The story will tell about an actual dinosaur dig.

JUST WAITING FOR YOU

Reading Fiction

Strategies:

MAKE INFERENCES
QUESTION
VISUALIZE
MAKE CONNECTIONS

MAKE INFERENCES

The author gives you hints about how a character feels about things.

I'll think about Coreena's reactions towards Mrs. Enfield.

What is Coreena's mood? How can you tell?

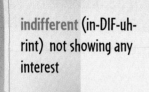

indifferent (in-DIF-uh-rint) not showing any interest

"Coreena?"

Coreena heard Mrs. Enfield calling her, even over the sound of the TV, but she didn't answer.

A moment later she heard her name again, this time spoken softly and right next to her ear. That *did* make her jump.

"What?" she snapped. Automatically, she turned the sound off with the remote. At every foster home she had stayed, someone was always telling her to turn down the volume, to turn off the TV altogether. Sometimes it was just an angry lecture about what was wrong with watching so much TV.

"Hi," said Mrs. Enfield. She smiled as she said it.

"Hi," answered Coreena. She kept her voice as **indifferent** as she could.

"There's something I want to show you . . . on the computer," she added as Coreena's attention wandered back to the jumpy movements of the silent cartoon characters on TV. Two short men in animal skins were climbing onto the back of a friendly dinosaur.

Mrs. Enfield moved across the room without looking back. She just assumed Coreena would follow. Coreena did, though she held back just long enough to make it clear that she did not want to.

She joined her new foster mother at the computer. Mrs. Enfield had another chair beside her own, but Coreena ignored it. She was not planning on staying.

"What do you think?" Mrs. Enfield asked, pointing at the screen. "I thought you'd like to see a real dinosaur."

Coreena found herself interested, **despite** herself. "What is it?" Of course, it was a dinosaur, or it had been. Actually, it was a drawing of a creature that, according to the scale shown beside it, had been huge.

"It's a computer **rendering** of a newly discovered plant-eating dinosaur. They're calling it *Paralititan*, which means "**tidal** giant."

"Wow!" said Coreena. She studied the picture. Mrs. Enfield scrolled down the screen and zoomed in on the Paralititan's statistics:

Length: 80–100 feet from snout to tail
Weight: up to 70 tons
Age: about 94 million years old
Period: Late Cretaceous
Where found: Egypt

Coreena finally sat down. Mrs. Enfield moved her chair slightly, and Coreena slid closer.

"You said it was newly discovered," Coreena asked, turning to Mrs. Enfield. "How can that be? I thought guys had dug up all these old bones already."

"Not at all," answered Mrs. Enfield as she clicked the mouse to bring up a new screen. This one showed a group of smiling young men and women. They were standing by the newly exposed bones of . . .

QUESTION
Ask yourself questions as you read: Who? What? When? Why? How? What if?

What's happening between Mrs. Enfield and Coreena?

Why would Mrs. Enfield call Coreena over to the computer?

despite (di-SPITE) in spite of, or not stopped by

rendering (REHN-duhr-ing) picture or model

tidal (TIDE-al) relating to ocean tides

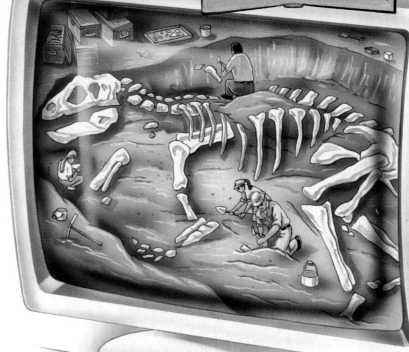

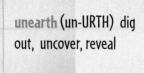

VISUALIZE

When Coreena thinks about her mother, she has a certain image in mind. What kind of picture do you have in your mind of Coreena's mom?

MAKE CONNECTIONS

Authors often connect new information to familiar information that readers know.

I know how Coreena felt at the beginning of the story and I know how she is feeling now.

Why have Coreena's feelings changed?

unearth (un-URTH) dig out, uncover, reveal

"The tidal giant!" Coreena yelled excitedly, pointing at the screen.

Mrs. Enfield nodded.

"Wow," Coreena said again. "So there are still dinosaurs nobody's ever seen before." She made it sound more like a question than a statement.

"There really are. Scientists **unearth** more every year," Mrs. Enfield said. She waved her hand toward the computer screen as she said "scientists."

Coreena was quiet a moment. She was thinking. Thinking about maybe being a dinosaur hunter someday. Thinking about sharing the idea with her mother as soon as Mom was well again.

"Mrs. Enfield?" said Coreena.

"Call me Mrs. E. That's what my kids have always called me." "My kids" she called them. Coreena knew she'd had only one kid, and she was now a grown woman. She had meant the foster children she had taken care of over the years.

"Mrs. E," said Coreena, smiling, "do you think there'll be any new ones left to find by the time I'm ready to be a dinosaur hunter?"

"Coreena, I think that somewhere there's a 'new' dinosaur that's been lying there for millions of years just waiting for you to discover it."

Understanding Fiction

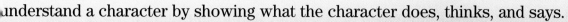

JUST WAITING FOR YOU

Visualize

The author helps readers understand a character by showing what the character does, thinks, and says.

Complete the character study chart below. For each character trait you describe, write the author's words that helped you see it. Go back to the text to find the words.

Author's Words

She kept her voice as indifferent as she could.

_____

Author's Words

_____
_____
_____

Trait
shyness
_____

Trait
_____
_____

Coreena

Trait
_____
_____

Trait
_____
_____

Author's Words

_____
_____
_____

Author's Words

_____
_____
_____

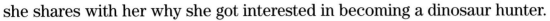

JUST WAITING FOR YOU

Summarize

Imagine that when Coreena
has a long visit with her mom,
she shares with her why she got interested in becoming a dinosaur hunter.
  Write how you think Coreena summarized the events for her mother.

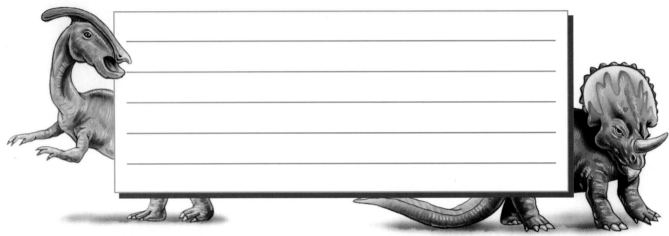

Determine What Is Important

You want to write a TV play based on Coreena's story of how she became interested in
hunting dinosaurs. First you have to convince a TV producer that your idea is a good one,
and you only have a few minutes to do so. Organize your thoughts about what you are going
to tell the TV producer by listing the major story points, or important ideas, in the story.

Story Points

_____

_____

_____

_____

_____

_____

_____

_____

Getting Ready

Have you ever tried putting together the pieces of a puzzle? Now imagine that the pieces are bones that have been scattered for millions of years. And if that doesn't make it hard enough, you don't even know what the final "picture" should look like.

INTERVIEW with a DINOSAUR HUNTER

Think About Genre

An interview with a real person is something like a biographical sketch. It gives factual information about that person's experience and achievements in his or her own words. The author, or person conducting the interview, includes information in the article that helps the reader get to know this person.

Based on the title of this selection— "An Interview with a Dinosaur Hunter"— which features can you expect to see? Fill in the bubble beside each possible answer choice.

Ⓐ questions an interviewer asked a dinosaur hunter

Ⓑ answers with factual information about dinosaurs

Ⓒ a how-to about how to make cartoon dinosaurs

Ⓓ factual information about a dinosaur hunter's life

Ⓔ a made-up story about dinosaurs that live now

Think About the Topic

Before reading a factual article, it is a good idea to ask some questions about the topic. Write a question you have about dinosaur hunters and dinosaurs.

_____

_____

_____

_____

Think Ahead

Glance ahead at the format, or setup, of this article. Predict how the format will give you information about the topic. Circle *True* or *False* for each statement.

1. The captions will have facts about the topic.　　**True　　False**

2. The answers will be based on important questions asked by the interviewer.　　**True　　False**

3. A graphic organizer will make information easier to understand.　　**True　　False**

INTERVIEW with a DINOSAUR HUNTER

MAKE CONNECTIONS

Nonfiction authors often connect new information to information that readers already know.

> I'll think about what I know about dinosaurs and what I have just read.

Which answer surprised you the most—the first or second? What did you think the answer was before you read it?

_____

_____

_____

_____

_____

paleontologist (pay-lee-ohn-TOH-loh-jist) one who studies the fossils (hardened remains) of life forms that existed millions of years ago

adapted from an article in _Odyssey_

Paul Sereno's expeditions as a paleontologist have taken him to Argentina, China, Mongolia, and Africa, where he has helped discover six new species (SPEE-sheez), or classes, of dinosaurs. This interview took place just before Paul Sereno left on yet another expedition that took him to the Sahara in Africa.

Odyssey: What do you think is the biggest misconception that people have about dinosaurs?

Paul Sereno: Well, most people think that all the dinosaurs lasted for the entire Mesozoic (meh-so-ZO-ik) Era and got snuffed out by an asteroid. That couldn't be further from the truth. Your average species lasted only a few million years, and new species arose all the time. It was a conveyor belt of species! The fact that different dinosaurs evolved on continents that had drifted apart is also news to a lot of people.

O: It seems as if several new species of dinosaurs are discovered each year. And they seem to be getting bigger and bigger. Is there any way to estimate how many new dinosaur species remain to be discovered?

P.S.: There are plenty more dinosaur species to be discovered. We seem to be entering a Golden Era of sorts for new species, with six or seven new ones being discovered each year. That rate will probably slow down after another 50 years [so maybe 300 more!].

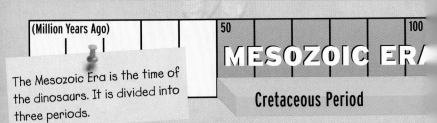

The Mesozoic Era is the time of the dinosaurs. It is divided into three periods.

MESOZOIC ERA

Cretaceous Period

Paleontologist Paul Sereno with a previously unknown dinosaur, the Spinosaur.

Q: What has been the most thrilling discovery of your career?

P.S.: When we found skeletons of a *Herrerasaurus*—a little-known flesh-eating theropod (THEH-ruh-pod)—against the odds, in Patagonia, Argentina. It was my first team—six young people joined me, and we found the earliest dinosaur on record, dating back to the middle Triassic Period, some 228 million years ago. Everyone said we couldn't do it, so after three weeks of searching, walking up to the skeleton—the way it was exposed with part of the skull and neck just visible on the surface of a rocky ledge—was the thrill of a lifetime!

Q: What is the most dangerous expedition that you've been on?

P.S.: The 1993 expedition to Niger [Africa] when we crossed the Sahara Desert twice, excavated six tons of dinosaur bone, and got it all back—as well as us—at the same time. That was a very exciting expedition!

Q: How do you actually search for dinosaur fossils?

P.S.: With legs, brains, and action. You need energy—lots of it; you need good legs. I like to go to places with good exposure—where there are dinosaur beds and outcroppings on the surface. You don't dig blindly. When you get into the area, you make appropriate strategic decisions based on fragments of fossils that you find. So *first* you have to find a bone, and that's where the team comes into play. Why does our team find fossils every time? Well, we take a *very young* crew that can walk incredible distances!

QUESTION

Ask yourself questions as you read: Who? What? When? Why? How? What if?

Why would an expedition in the Sahara be especially dangerous?

How did you answer the above question?

_____
_____
_____
_____
_____
_____
_____

excavated (EKS-kuh-vayt-id) dug out

outcropping (OUT-crohp-ihng) fossils or other materials that pushed to the surface of the earth

	150				200				250

Jurassic Period   Triassic Period

evolution (ev-oh-LOO-shin) gradual change over time

Some scientists think the ancestor of today's birds may be the ARCHAEOPTERYX (ahr-kee-OHP-tuh-riks). What do you think?

O: How do you analyze the newly extracted fossils?
P.S.: Well, first I describe the specimens that are new to science, but ultimately it's the big patterns of evolution that I'm after, such as why these animals evolved where they did and ultimately how they fit into the big pattern of evolution.

O: What advice can you give to [young people] who are fascinated by dinosaurs and would love to have a career in paleontology?
P.S.: Well, I think you can be whatever you want to be as long as you give yourself a chance. Find the talents that are locked inside you just under your skin. You can begin to do that by volunteering in labs and museums or by joining a group that is going into the field. In school, take lots of science—from math to biology—and also take art.

O: Finally, everyone fantasizes about living with the dinosaurs. If they had survived and evolved to be highly intelligent creatures, what do you think would have happened?
P.S.: We already know! They're with us. They live as birds. Birds have big brains and they are intelligent. That's indeed what dinosaurs have evolved into. We always tend to think of "we," or something like "us," as the end point of evolution. No way! Dinosaurs are with us today. Their descendants are birds, and that's perfectly acceptable.

Archaeopteryx   **modern crow**

Visualize

All the questions in "Interview with a Dinosaur Hunter" are related to several important ideas.

To complete the graphic organizer below, number the interview questions 1–8. Then, next to each important idea, list the numbers of the questions that relate to that idea.

Main Idea
Paul Sereno loves his work as a paleontologist.

_____

Important Idea A
He has discovered new species.

_____

Important Idea B
His expeditions have taken him all around the world.

_____

Important Idea C
His finds help scientists understand dinosaurs better.

_____

Important Idea D
Young people can get involved as dinosaur hunters.

_____

INTERVIEW with a DINOSAUR HUNTER

Summarize

Perhaps you are thinking of becoming a dinosaur hunter. What knowledge and skills will you need?

Summarize Paul Sereno's responses to create a description of the knowledge and skills a young paleontologist will need.

WANTED:

PALEONTOLOGIST

Are you interested in becoming a dinosaur hunter? Candidates for Paul Sereno's next dinosaur dig should have the following knowledge and skills:

Determine What Is Important

A newspaper headline pulls out the most important idea from an article in as few words as possible.

Choose Paul Sereno's answers to the interviewer's questions that tell about the most important things he has done. Then write a headline for each one. Try to have about 36 letters, spaces, and punctuation marks in each headline. An example has been done for you.

1. | N | E | W | | D | I | N | O | S | A | U | R | | S | P | E | C | I | E | S | | F | O | U | N | D | | E | A | C | H | | Y | E | A | R |

2.

3.

4.

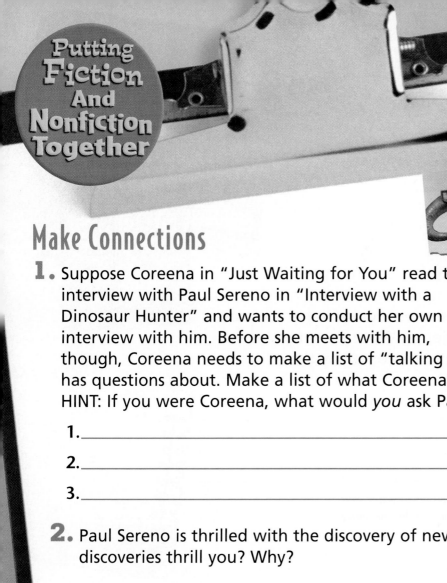

Make Connections

1. Suppose Coreena in "Just Waiting for You" read the interview with Paul Sereno in "Interview with a Dinosaur Hunter" and wants to conduct her own interview with him. Before she meets with him, though, Coreena needs to make a list of "talking points"—things she has questions about. Make a list of what Coreena's talking points might be. HINT: If you were Coreena, what would *you* ask Paul Sereno?

1._____

2._____

3._____

2. Paul Sereno is thrilled with the discovery of new dinosaurs. What kinds of discoveries thrill you? Why?

_____

_____

_____

3. Coreena, in "Just Waiting for You," is a character in a piece of realistic fiction. What is it about her that makes her seem realistic to you?

_____

_____

_____

4. What do you think Coreena and Paul Sereno have in common? Explain.

_____

_____

_____

Write a Journal Entry

Imagine an older Coreena going on an expedition with Paul Sereno and other young men and women. After each day's work, she makes sure to write in her journal, describing that day's experience. Write an entry she, or anyone in the group, might write on a day they discover some new dinosaur bones.

_____

_____

_____

BLACKLINE MASTER Before you write, use the Blackline Master your teacher will give you to plan your journal entry.

Today we found what we were looking for!

Plan Your Research

One of the most exciting things about dinosaur hunting is that discoveries are made all the time. If you want to keep up with them, you have to do your research faithfully. Make a list of the questions you hope to have answered and begin your research.

_____

_____

_____

_____

_____

_____

_____

Net Connection

http://www.projectexploration.org/mongolia/

Getting Ready

Danger AT THE Bottom OF THE World

The southern-most spot on Earth is the large, icy continent of Antarctica. Even the simplest day-to-day tasks can be dangerous because Antarctica's climate is colder than cold! The 3,000 people who live there try to be prepared for anything. How does one mechanic manage in such a harsh environment?

Think About Genre

"Danger at the Bottom of the World" is realistic fiction. It is based on facts and tells about events that could really happen. It is told in the first person. This means that the main character is telling the story. It is as if you could hear the author talking directly to you about himself or herself.

Mark the sentence you are most likely to find in a story told in the first person.

(A) She added half a cup of oil, and stirred the mix well.

(B) I never could find enough to read about Antarctica.

(C) As the wind blew, Paul pulled his coat more tightly about him.

(D) Marny's Dad thinks people should eat more fish.

Think About the Topic

Read the introduction to "Danger at the Bottom of the World." Think of what you already know about Antarctica. Write T or F next to each statement.

1. _____ Its warm, tropical winds make Antarctica a perfect vacation spot.

2. _____ Antarctica is home to a variety of wildlife, including penguins and whales.

3. _____ The South Pole is located in Antarctica.

4. _____ In the late 1800s, lots of people began moving to Antarctica because of the pleasant climate.

Think Ahead

Reread the introduction. Think about the genre and what you know about the topic. Then flip through the story. On the lines below, write what you think "Danger at the Bottom of the World" is about.

_____

_____

_____

_____

_____

_____

Reading
Fiction

Strategies:
MAKE CONNECTIONS
QUESTION
MAKE INFERENCES
UNDERSTAND GENRE

MAKE CONNECTIONS
Whenever you can, make connections between story events and events in real life.

What is different about this July 4?

UNDERSTANDING GENRE

How can you tell this is written in the first person? Who is telling the story?

central government
(SEN-trul GOV-ern-mint)
main control over a country, state, or city

Danger AT THE Bottom OF THE World

July 4

Dear Jasmine,

It's about 2 P.M. on the Fourth of July. Of course, here at the South Pole it's pitch dark and −60°F. The howling wind makes an awful noise.

There's no other place like Antarctica. Did you know there is no **central government**? Instead, twenty-seven countries run scientific research stations here. McMurdo Station is run by the United States. There are about 50 of us, including scientists, mechanics, and helpers.

We are all sharing our barbecue and fireworks memories today. Of course, neither of those is allowed. Antarctica is so dry that fire is a real danger. (Who'd think that an ice-covered continent could also be a desert?)

We try to be respectful of each other's space. Everyone is having a tough time because we are stuck indoors during the winter—and it's winter here now, even though it's July. We're the opposite of you, remember? We have six months of cold and darkness, so we don't need extra reasons to get on each other's nerves.

There's a lot to do. We can bowl, use a gym, and go to classes and lectures. I miss seeing the sun. We have a chart where we mark off the days until the sun rises again—September 22. Only 80 days away!

Love,
Evan

August 15

Dear Jasmine,

I'm writing to you from the **infirmary**. Before you worry, please know that I am fine. I have a sprained ankle and two **fractured** ribs. It could have been worse!

You remember that I'm on the repair crew. We keep the snowmobiles, diving equipment, batteries, and so on, in good working condition for the scientists. One "day" (if you can break this endless night into days) I discovered that I ran out of fuel for the snowmobiles.

I knew I'd have to brave the weather outside in order to get a barrel of fuel from the storage area. I took the only snowmobile that still had a full tank, told my buddies where I was going, and set out.

Weather changes very suddenly here. Within five minutes, gusts of icy wind were blowing so strongly that I lost control of the snowmobile, and it rolled over, with me in it! At least I was going slowly. That's because the speed limit at McMurdo Station is 15 miles per hour.

I radioed for help and tried to stay calm. I knew that a few minutes more in the **extreme** cold could be very dangerous. The rescuers knew that, too. They were at my side in less than five minutes, wrapping me in special blankets, and driving me over to the infirmary.

Imagine a place so cold that ten minutes outside can threaten your life! That's the South Pole. It's like being on another planet. But I love it here, even with its risks!

Love,
Evan

QUESTION

Remember to stop now and then and ask yourself questions about the story. Read the questions below. Decide whether they tell about the plot, the character, or the setting. Fill in the circle in front of the correct answer.

1. Where is Evan when he writes to Jasmine on August 15?

(A) character

(B) plot

(C) setting

2. Now choose the *actual* answer to this question. Where is Evan when he writes to Jasmine on August 15?

(A) a snowmobile

(B) the infirmary

(C) Building 188

extreme (ek-STREEM) strong, great, intense

fractured (FRAK-chured) broken or cracked, especially a bone

infirmary (in-FUR-mur-ree) center for medical services, small hospital

Sometimes authors expect you to "read between the lines." To do that, find clues from the story and add them to what you already know.

What season is September, if January is summer in Antarctica? Look at the **date** and the **first two paragraphs**.

midsummer (mid-SUM-ur) time of year when the days are longest

September 22

Dear Jasmine,

The sun is back! What a celebration we had! It was a short day, though, since the first day lasts only a few minutes. But I know the days will get longer.

Are you going to visit in January? That's tourist season. It will be **midsummer** here, which means constant daylight. You'd see seals, penguins, whales, and more.

Some people say Antarctica makes you feel small. I disagree. I think it makes you feel part of the world in a way that no other place can.

Love,
Evan

Danger AT THE Bottom OF THE World

Visualize

Read the words and phrases in the boxes. Three tell about the setting, and three tell about the plot of "Danger at the Bottom of the World." Complete the graphic organizer by writing the correct word or phrase in each balloon.

| snowmobile accident | winter | needs to get fuel |
| dark | cold and windy | sudden storm begins |

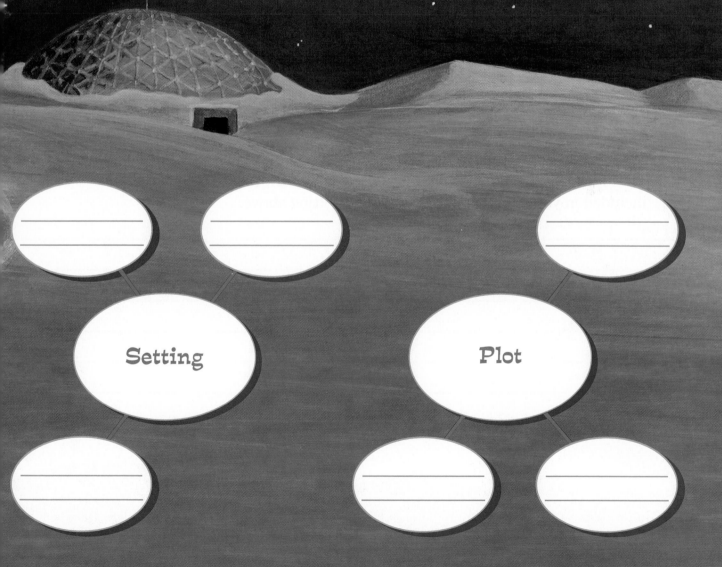

Setting

Plot

Summarize

Write a summary of the setting and the plot of the story "Danger at the Bottom of the World" using the details you wrote in the "Visualize" graphic organizer on page 121.

_____
_____
_____
_____
_____
_____
_____
_____

Determine What Is Important

Look back through the story. When you come to a part you think is important, underline or highlight the words. On the lines below, write some of the points you marked that were NOT included in your summary of the plot and setting above.

_____
_____
_____
_____
_____

Getting Ready

In Antarctica, the winters are so harsh that planes don't usually land at that time of year. This can be a problem when there is an emergency and someone *has* to get out. Read what happened when it was necessary to do the nearly "impossible" in order to save a life.

ANTARCTICA: Continent Without a Hospital

Think About Genre

Newspapers report the news, but they often state opinions, too. In order to keep the "news" separate from "opinions," there is a type of article called an editorial. An editorial gives an opinion and tries to persuade others to agree.

Editorials begin by stating the writer's opinion about a news topic. The writer tries to convince others to agree by providing supporting evidence as well as giving reasons against other people's arguments.

Which of the following sentences might you find in an editorial? Fill in the circle in front of the best choice.

Ⓐ Janelle McClennan should be the next mayor of this city.

Ⓑ Tomorrow's weather will be partly cloudy with showers.

Ⓒ A runoff election for school board chair will be held on June 11.

Ⓓ Last night's concert was a sell-out.

Think About the Topic

You read about Antarctica's special features in "Danger at the Bottom of the World." Ask yourself, *What's so special about Antarctica?* Write as many features as you can on the lines below.

_____

_____

_____

_____

Think Ahead

Flip through the editorial on the following pages. Look at the headings, maps, and photographs. Try to decide what the editorial will be about. Fill in the blanks to complete the sentences.

The editorial will be about the continent

of _____. The opinion stated will

probably be about _____

because _____

_____.

ANTARCTICA: Continent Without a Hospital

VISUALIZE

As you read, it may help you to be familiar with where Antarctica is. I will find a world map or a globe and locate Antarctica. Then I'll find New Zealand and finally, Chile in South America.

Compare these places to where you live. How far are they from your home? From other continents?

_____

_____

_____

_____

airlifted (AIR-lif-ted) taken out or brought in by airplane

continent (KON-tih-nent) one of the main land masses on Earth

under-equipped (UN-der ee-KWIPT) not having all the things one needs in order to do the work one is supposed to do

How can an entire continent exist without a proper hospital? In Antarctica, that is the situation—a situation that is dangerous and must change.

What Happens When the Doctor Needs a Doctor?

On Thursday, April 26, 2001, a small plane airlifted Dr. Ronald S. Shemenski out of Antarctica. He was seriously ill. He urgently needed to get to the United States, 9,000 miles away, to receive medical care. Dr. Shemenski was also the only doctor for a staff of the 50 Americans working in Antarctica. If he couldn't work due to his own illness, they would have had no doctor.

The rescue was heroic. For one thing, Antarctica was "closed for the winter." The huge continent was already in near-total darkness. Temperatures were already –60°F. The runway for the plane was lit by rows of steel drums filled with burning garbage.

After the plane landed, the crew refueled and kept an eye on the weather. During the ten hours they had to wait until it was safe to leave, they used heaters to blow warm air over the aircraft. This was necessary to keep the fuel from freezing.

Dr. Shemenski was successfully airlifted out of Antarctica. Those who flew him out deserve the highest praise.

People realized that there was a serious problem: Antarctica is medically under-equipped. The facilities must be expanded and improved.

Dr. Ronald S. Shemenski

Kenn Borek Air Ltd.

Wilderness or Laboratory?

Journalists and tour guides like to paint Antarctica as the last truly wild, open, empty place on our planet. They describe the extreme climate. For example, Antarctica's **mean annual temperature** is –56°F. Nighttime lasts for months.

It turns out that the land is not as empty and wild as you might think. In all, about 3,000 people from 42 countries live in Antarctica. Antarctica's residents drive gas-powered vehicles, use electricity, produce garbage, and build shelters. Yet there was only one doctor (and now his replacement, Dr. Betty Carlisle) for 50 American researchers. The infirmary was not set up for a serious medical condition like his.

How can this be? Antarctica has no central government. Each nation has its own area on the continent. If the United States is going to run its little slice of Antarctica like a 19th-century frontier-town, it may attract thrill-seekers rather than serious researchers.

This might affect the quality of the research. It is very important research. Many of the studies in Antarctica gather information about the earth's climate, including the effects of global warming and pollution. Don't we want only the best people working on this very important issue? Why should they come if they cannot be sure they will have good medical care?

UNDERSTAND GENRE
(editorial)

Editorials present arguments so that readers are persuaded to share the opinions of the writers. What opinion is expressed in this editorial? Complete the sentence.

Antarctica needs better

_____

_____

_____

Write one argument the author gives to support this opinion.

_____

_____

mean annual temperature (meen AN-yoo-wul TEM-pruh-chur) A year's worth of daily temperature readings added together and divided by 365.

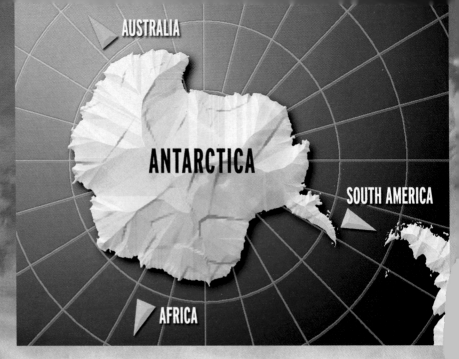

AUSTRALIA

ANTARCTICA

SOUTH AMERICA

AFRICA

UNDERSTANDING GENRE

As part of an argument, the author compares Antarctica to Mars. How does this get the idea across that Antarctica is a distant, dangerous place? Why would this be an argument for improving Antarctica's medical care?

_____

_____

MAKE INFERENCES

Clues help you figure out words that are not familiar. Find the word **remote**. Read the sentences before and after the word. What words help you infer where Antarctica is in the world?

_____

_____

_____

remote (rih-MOHT)
far away in distance

state-of-the-art
the latest development
or invention

They'd Never Get Away With This on Mars

"We might as well be on Mars . . ." one of the flight crew said of this continent, the driest, coldest place on earth. However, we doubt that a Mars station would be as medically unprepared as this one. Why? Because planners of a Mars station would understand the need for a state-of-the-art hospital in a faraway outpost.

Antarctica's planners did not realize how remote this settlement really is. It is far away in distance, and it is far away if you have to get someone or something in or out in a hurry.

It is time to face facts: Antarctica is not a wilderness and people are there to stay. This is as certain as the ice and bitter cold. Anyone who signs up to do scientific research in Antarctica has the right to the same medical care he or she could have back home. Therefore, medical services must be improved and expanded. This dangerous situation must end.

Winter-over Crew 1996/97,
Amundsen-Scott South Pole
Station, Antarctica

Dr. Betty Carlisle,
Dr. Shemenski's
replacement

ANTARCTICA:
Continent Without a Hospital

Visualize

A number of problems are mentioned in this editorial. Read the problem and the actions in the chart. Then fill in the boxes under the heading, "Results."

Problem

There is no major hospital in Antarctica, only an infirmary. Winter had already arrived when Dr. Shemenski had to be rescued.

Action
What solution did people try to find?

Results
What happened because of this solution?

ANTARCTICA:
Continent Without a Hospital

Summarize

The format of "Antarctica: Continent Without a Hospital" is similar to an information article, except that it states opinions as well as facts. The summary below is set up like a list. Read each statement. If it is an opinion, write **O**. If it is a fact, write **F**.

1. _____ Antarctica needs better medical care.

2. _____ In April, 2001, there was a medical emergency that could not be treated at their infirmary.

3. _____ The patient was the doctor for the American crew.

4. _____ Airlifting the patient out of Antarctica was difficult.

5. _____ The crew which managed the airlift braved dangerous conditions to land and take off again.

6. _____ Unless medical care gets better in Antarctica, the best scientists will not want to come.

7. _____ If medical care doesn't improve in Antarctica, future research will be endangered.

Determine What Is Important

List each of the headings in the editorial at the top of each column. Next to each **I**, write an important detail. Next to each **U**, write an unimportant detail.

1.	2.	3.
I	I	I
U	U	U
I	I	I
U	U	U

Flags of many nations and signposts stand at the South Pole, Antarctica

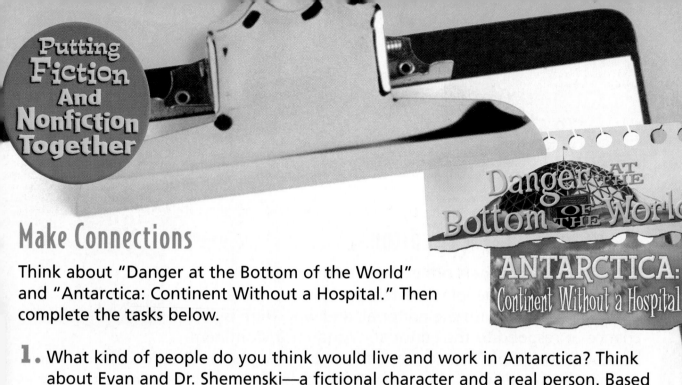

Make Connections

Think about "Danger at the Bottom of the World" and "Antarctica: Continent Without a Hospital." Then complete the tasks below.

1. What kind of people do you think would live and work in Antarctica? Think about Evan and Dr. Shemenski—a fictional character and a real person. Based upon what you have read and what you already know, make a list of personality traits that both characters share.

_____

_____

_____

_____

2. Think about both selections and where the stories are set. What would you find hardest about living in Antarctica? What would you find interesting?

_____

_____

_____

_____

3. If you won a free trip to Antarctica during their summer season, would you go? Explain your answer. If you said yes, what would you plan to see and do?

_____

_____

_____

_____

Write a Letter to the Editor

Oftentimes newspapers print letters to the editor. The letters are sent by people who tell the editor whether they agree or disagree with the editorial, and why. Here is your chance to respond to the editorial, "Antarctica: Continent Without a Hospital." Think about whether you agree or disagree with it. Plan your reply as a letter to the editor. Begin by writing a topic sentence that states your opinion. Then list a few arguments to support your point of view.

_____

_____

_____

_____

_____

BLACKLINE MASTER Before you write, use the Blackline Master your teacher will give you to plan your response.

Plan Your Research

You may wish to follow up on the story of Dr. Shemenski's rescue. You can visit the website below and click on "medevac" for press releases describing the airlift, pictures of Dr. Shemenski and Dr. Carlisle, and other articles about this event. You can also write to the press contact, whose name is listed at the site. Write three things you would like to investigate.

_____

_____

_____

_____

Net Connection

http://www.southpolestation.com

Getting Ready

his lesson is a test. After you read "A Monumental ystery," you will be asked questions about the election. These questions will test how well you nderstand genre. They will also test how well you an use the reading strategies you have practiced: etermine Important Ideas, Summarize, ake Connections, Question, ake Inferences, and Visualize.

A MONUMENTAL MYSTERY

merican monuments mark important oments in U.S. history. But what if the istory of the monument itself is a ystery? To find the solution, we have o dig into the past for the clues that ill answer our questions.

hink About Genre

Monumental Mystery," as its name ggests, is a kind of fiction known as a ystery story, where characters use clues solve a puzzle, or mystery. Think about ystery stories you have read. On the es below, write one thing that you pect to find in a mystery.

_____

_____

_____

_____

Think About the Topic

Read the above introduction to "A Monumental Mystery." Ask yourself: *What do I know about monuments? Where are some of the most important ones located? What do I know about the people who built them?* Write two things you know on the lines below.

_____

_____

_____

Think Ahead

Take a quick look at the story. Think about the title, illustrations, and time line. Think about what you wrote about the topic. Make a prediction. Tell what you think you will read about in "A Monumental Mystery."

_____

_____

_____

A MONUMENTAL MYSTERY

immigration (ihm-ih-GRAY-shuhn) the coming into one country by people from another country

monumental (mohn-yoo-MEHN-til) about a monument; huge

whimper (WIHM-pur) a cry or sob

Crash!

Ernesto listened after the noise stopped echoing overhead. He expected to hear a cry for help or a **whimper** of pain. But all he heard was the trap door to the attic being replaced and Nathan's footsteps on the ladder.

"You okay?" asked Ernesto. Nathan was holding a thick folder of papers under one arm and rubbing a spot on his head with his other hand.

"I'm okay. I was reaching for this box of papers on top of a huge case, and it turned out to be heavier than I expected. Lucky I have a hard head," he added, laughing.

Ernesto laughed, too. He was glad his friend was okay. He was pleased to get Nathan as his partner for this **immigration** project for school, but he did not want him to get hurt working on it.

"Let's look at this stuff," said Nathan as he put the folder down on his bed. It was dusty from years in the attic, but the writing on it was still readable. It said, "Letters of Harry Edelstein, 1876–1898."

For their project on American monuments, Mr. Chou had suggested researching family members who had passed through New York City when they came to the United States. He was interested in whether any o

1875 Sculptor Frédéric-Auguste Bartholdi begins construction of the statue in France, hoping it will be ready by 1876, the hundredth anniversary of the Declaration of Independence.

1876 Bartholdi, behind schedule, sends what he has finished to the United States: the completed right hand and torch. They are displayed at the Centennial Exposition in Philadelphia and later in New York City before being returned to France.

hem had written diary entries or letters that
nentioned seeing the Statue of Liberty, in Upper
New York Bay, or described what it meant to them
t the time.

Nathan's mother directed them to the attic to look
or family papers. She knew exactly where the earliest
nes were. They all had to do with Great-Uncle Harry,
ne first family member to reach the United States.
he boys also had planned to interview Ernesto's
buela. Then Ernesto found out that his grandmother
rrived in the United States on a plane to Miami,
lorida.

Opening the folder, Nathan took out the first letter
nd unfolded it carefully. The paper was thin and
eemed quite **brittle**. At the top of the page, he could
nake out the year. It was 1876!

"What does it say?" asked Ernesto, excitement in
is voice.

Nathan looked closely at the paper and finally said
n a dull voice, "I can't tell. It's in some language I
on't know. The letters don't look like anything I've
ver seen."

The boys looked at each other, puzzled, then finally
ent downstairs to get help from Mr. and Mrs.
delstein.

They were able to solve the mystery, sort of. The
anguage was Russian, but neither Harriet nor Ben
delstein knew how to **translate** it. Finally, Mr.
delstein remembered that a neighbor, Mrs. Genkina
ame from Russia.

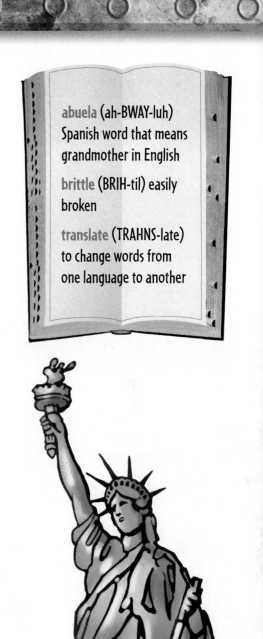

abuela (ah-BWAY-luh)
Spanish word that means
grandmother in English

brittle (BRIH-til) easily
broken

translate (TRAHNS-late)
to change words from
one language to another

885 The 214 separate
parts of Liberty
rive in the United States
wooden crates.

1886 The assembled
monument
is dedicated in Upper
New York Bay.

The next day Mrs. Genkina began **dictating** a translation of the letter. Ernesto wrote the words down because Nathan was too excited. The letter had been written by Great-Uncle Harry—actually, Nathan's great, great, great-uncle—to Harry's own mother back in Russia. And it did indeed mention the Statue of Liberty.

The only problem was that what the letter said did not make sense.

"Read that line to me again," said Nathan when they were back at his house.

"'I did get to see the famous Miss Liberty when I came to New York City,'" read Ernesto. "'but only a little bit of her. Someday I hope that together we will see all of her.'"

Ernesto looked puzzled. "What does he mean he saw only a little bit of her? She's so big!"

Nathan **shrugged** his shoulders. Then he snapped his fingers. He had an idea. So did Ernesto. In one voice they said, "The encyclopedia!"

It did not take the boys long to figure out the answer to Ernesto's question once they read the time line for Miss Liberty.

The boys used a time line to solve the mystery. Can you use the same information to solve it, too?

dictating (DIK-tayt-ing) saying words as another person writes them down

shrugged (SHRUHGD) to raise the shoulders to show uncertainty

A MONUMENTAL MYSTERY

For numbers 1 through 6 use the strategies you learned and fill in the letter of the sentence that best answers the question.

1. A question you might have asked is: *How do you think the Edelsteins get Great-Uncle Harry's letters?* **(QUESTION STRATEGY)**

   Ⓐ Great-Uncle Harry made two copies and saved one.

   Ⓑ Great-Uncle Harry's mother saved the letters and passed them on.

   Ⓒ Great-Uncle Harry never mailed any of the letters.

   Ⓓ After his mother came to the United States, Great-Uncle Harry wrote down what he could remember.

2. What topic do you think Ernesto and Nathan looked up in the library? **(MAKE INFERENCES STRATEGY)**

   Ⓐ Great-Uncle Harry

   Ⓑ the year 1876

   Ⓒ the Statue of Liberty

   Ⓓ New York City

3. What feature makes this story a mystery? **(UNDERSTAND GENRE STRATEGY)**

   Ⓐ There are clues to solving the mystery.

   Ⓑ We know that the main characters are detectives.

   Ⓒ All the events really happened.

   Ⓓ None of the events or people are realistic.

4. Which clue on the time line would NOT help Nathan and Ernesto solve the mystery of why Great-Uncle Harry saw only a little part of Liberty in 1876? **(DETERMINE WHAT IS IMPORTANT STRATEGY)**

   Ⓐ Frédéric-Auguste Bartholdi begins construction of the statue in France in 1875.

   Ⓑ The 214 parts of Liberty arrive in the United States in 1885.

   Ⓒ The monument is dedicated in 1886.

   Ⓓ Only the completed right hand and torch are displayed at the Centennial Exposition in Philadelphia in 1876.

5. What do you think Nathan and Ernesto imagine about Great-Uncle Harry's arrival to New York? **(VISUALIZE STRATEGY)**

(A) They imagine a plane landing near the harbor.

(B) They imagine an over-crowded boat of people trying to get a glimpse of the Statue of Liberty.

(C) They see a few people on a ferry.

(D) They imagine a fancy ship the size of the Titanic coming into the harbor.

6. Reread paragraph 4 on page 134. What did Great-Uncle Harry mean when he wrote this to his mother: *Someday I hope that together we will see all of her?* **(MAKE INFERENCES STRATEGY)**

(A) He plans to send pictures of the statue to his mother in Russia.

(B) He wants to travel around the United States with his mother.

(C) He is going back to Russia to see his mother.

(D) He hopes to bring his mother to the United States.

For question 7, use the strategies you learned to complete your response.

7. As briefly as possible, summarize the story of "A Monumental Mystery."
(DETERMINE WHAT IS IMPORTANT STRATEGY, SUMMARIZE STRATEGY)

_____

_____

_____

_____

_____

_____

_____

_____

STOP This is the end of the test for "A Monumental Mystery."
When your teacher tells you, go on to read the next selection, "A Mighty Woman."

Getting Ready

This lesson is a test. After you read "A Mighty Woman," you will be asked questions about the selection. These questions will test how well you understand genre. They will also test how well you can use the reading strategies you have practiced: Determine Important Ideas, Summarize, Make Connections, Question, Make Inferences, and Visualize.

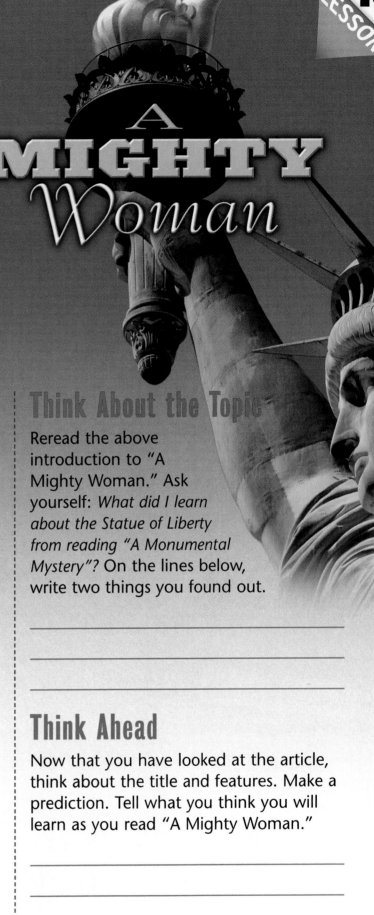

A MIGHTY Woman

She faces the world, too big to be missed. Nor can you miss her message. Her name is Liberty, and that is her message, too.

Think About Genre

Informational articles often include certain features. Take a quick look at "A Mighty Woman." Which features does it contain? Put a check beside each one.

☐ photographs or realistic artwork

☐ captions that provide extra information

☐ headings that tell about each section in the article

☐ graphic aids, such as maps, graphs, charts, diagrams, or time lines

☐ directions or steps in a process

Think About the Topic

Reread the above introduction to "A Mighty Woman." Ask yourself: *What did I learn about the Statue of Liberty from reading "A Monumental Mystery"?* On the lines below, write two things you found out.

_____

_____

_____

Think Ahead

Now that you have looked at the article, think about the title and features. Make a prediction. Tell what you think you will learn as you read "A Mighty Woman."

_____

_____

_____

A MIGHTY Woman

Right hand and the torch at the Centennial Exposition in Philadelphia. 1876

Frédéric-Auguste Bartholdi

The Statue of Liberty is one of the largest statues ever built. More than just a statue, though, it is also a monumental symbol. It is what this statue represents— the idea it stands for—that makes it one of the most welcome sights in the world.

The Idea

During the American Revolution (1775 –1783), American colonists fought to gain their freedom from England. The government of France took sides in that war, sending aid to the Americans. France's help was important to America's victory.

About 90 years after that war began, a Frenchman suggested building a monument to celebrate the ideal of liberty. It would also honor the friendship between France and the United States of America.

The Sculptor

A few years later, in 1871, a well-known French sculptor, Frédéric-Auguste Bartholdi (fray-day-REEK oh-GOOST bar-TOHL-dee) sailed to the United States. He had two reasons for making the trip. One was to urge Americans to get behind the project. Another was to find the best place to build the monument.

ideal (eye-DEEL) dream of, or best example of, something

symbol (SIHM-bul) something that stands for an idea

Manhattan

Ellis Island

Liberty Island

Bartholdi chose Bedloe's Island, not far from the tip of Manhattan. The island was named after Isaac Bedloe, the man who owned it in the 1600s. At one time Bedloe's Island held a fort that protected New York City against attack by enemy ships.

The Symbol

After Bartholdi returned to France, he began to draw the statue he saw in his mind. He wanted it to be huge. In his design, the ideal of liberty would be represented by the proud figure of a woman holding a torch. Bartholdi wanted the torch to work like a lighthouse, guiding ships to a safe harbor and lighting the way to liberty for new arrivals.

Other parts of the statue are also symbolic. The seven spikes on its crown stand for the light of liberty shining on the seven seas and seven continents. In her left arm, Liberty holds a tablet with the date of the Declaration of Independence. At her feet lies a broken chain that represents the escape from tyrannical rulers. The woman's face, however, is based on a real person. Bartholdi used his own mother as the model.

The Statue

France raised about $400,000 for the statue, while people in the United States raised money for the pedestal. American architect (AHR-kih-tekt) Richard Morris Hunt was chosen to design it.

Bartholdi had hoped to have the entire statue ready by 1876, the hundredth anniversary of the signing of the Declaration of Independence. But this was impossible. So instead, he sent the right hand and the torch to the Centennial Exposition in Philadelphia, where the Declaration had been signed. The hand and the torch were then sent on to New York City, which would be its final home.

pedestal (PEH-dih-stuhl) base

symbolic (sihm-BOH-lik) standing for ideas

tyrannical (tih-RAH-nih-kahl) unfair use of power

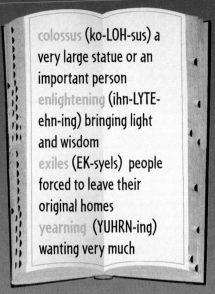

colossus (ko-LOH-sus) a very large statue or an important person

enlightening (ihn-LYTE-ehn-ing) bringing light and wisdom

exiles (EK-syels) people forced to leave their original homes

yearning (YUHRN-ing) wanting very much

The Poem

The statue—whose full name was Liberty Enlightening the World—was finally ready in 1886. The city celebrated with a great parade. President Grover Cleveland was there, as was Bartholdi and other French citizens who had taken part in the project.

Though the statue would always mark the friendship between the United States and France, it came to mean other things as well. One reason for this is a poem by Emma Lazarus (LAH-zuh-rus), called "The New Colossus." This poem was added to the pedestal in 1903.

The Statue of Liberty greeted millions of people as they passed it on the way to the immigration station on Ellis Island. In writing of Liberty, the poet Emma Lazarus speaks of "A mighty woman with a torch" and calls her "Mother of Exiles." She imagines the statue calling out a welcome to newcomers. And she puts the following words into Liberty's mouth:

"Give me your tired, your poor,
Your huddled masses yearning to breathe free...
Send them to me, she cries, as I lift my lamp beside the golden door!"

Ellis Island no longer receives immigrants, but all those who passed through are remembered in the Museum of Immigration, which opened there in 1990. And Ellis Island and Liberty Island (as it has been called since 1956) will forever be linked. Together they form the Statue of Liberty National Monument.

Sonnets.

I.

The New Colossus.

Not like the brazen giant of Greek fame,
With conquering limbs astride from land to land;
Here at our sea-washed, sunset gates shall stand
A mighty woman with a torch, whose flame
Is the imprisoned lightning, and her name
Mother of Exiles. From her beacon-hand
Glows world-wide...

Emma Lazarus
author of "The New Colossus"

Testing Your Understanding

For numbers 1 through 6, use the strategies you have learned and fill in the letter of the sentence that best answers the question.

1. The article tells about events that happened over a period of time. Which time period does it cover? **(DETERMINE WHAT IS IMPORTANT STRATEGY)**

   Ⓐ all of a French sculptor's life

   Ⓑ the years it took to put up a monument

   Ⓒ the time it took to write the poem "The Colossus"

   Ⓓ the first 100 years of the United States

2. A question you might have asked is: *Why do you think Bartholdi used his mother as a model for the Statue of Liberty?* **(QUESTION STRATEGY)**

   Ⓐ He loved and respected her.

   Ⓑ The Americans asked him to.

   Ⓒ She was a very tall woman.

   Ⓓ His French supporters thought it would be a good idea.

3. Another question you might have asked is: *Why do you think it was important for Bartholdi to send the hand and torch to the Centennial Exposition?* **(QUESTION STRATEGY)**

   Ⓐ The people who paid for the statue insisted on it.

   Ⓑ A group of Americans paid him to send it.

   Ⓒ The whole statue wouldn't fit on a ship.

   Ⓓ He wanted to have something there for the Centennial Exposition.

4. Which part is NOT a symbol of what the Statue of Liberty meant to new immigrants? **(DETERMINE WHAT IS IMPORTANT STRATEGY)**

   Ⓐ the poem by Emma Lazarus

   Ⓑ the crown

   Ⓒ the statue's face

   Ⓓ the broken chain

5. Millions of immigrants saw the Statue of Liberty on their way to Ellis Island. What might you visualize happening on the ships as they came into the harbor? (VISUALIZE STRATEGY)

(A) Most people just go about their regular business.

(B) People stand at the ship's rail to see the statue.

(C) The captain of the ship tells people to go to their cabins.

(D) The sailors on the ship raise the American flag.

6. What do you think Emma Lazarus meant by the phrase "the golden door"? (MAKE INFERENCES STRATEGY)

(A) There is a gold-colored door leading to the inside of the statue.

(B) Newcomers could make a lot of money in their new country.

(C) Sunlight made the statue look like gold.

(D) Coming to America is a "door" to a new world and a better life.

For question 7, use the strategies you learned to complete your response.

7. As briefly as possible, summarize the story of "A Mighty Woman." (DETERMINE WHAT IS IMPORTANT STRATEGY, SUMMARIZE STRATEGY)

_____

_____

_____

_____

_____

_____

_____

_____

_____

STOP This is the end of the test for "A Mighty Woman."
When your teacher tells you, go on to finish the last part of the test.

For numbers 1 through 3, fill in the letter of the sentence that best answers the question. For number 4, write a few sentences.

1. Which one of the following statements tells how the two selections are alike? (MAKE CONNECTIONS STRATEGY)

   Ⓐ They both take place in the 1800s.

   Ⓑ They both tell why so many people came to the United States from Russia.

   Ⓒ They both cover a time period of about 100 years.

   Ⓓ They both deal with the setting up of the Statue of Liberty.

2. Which of the following statements from "A Monumental Mystery" fits in with the facts of history in "A Mighty Woman"? (MAKE CONNECTIONS STRATEGY)

   Ⓐ Mr. Chou was interested in which people saw the Statue of Liberty.

   Ⓑ Great-Uncle Harry got to see only a small part of the Statue of Liberty when he arrived in New York City.

   Ⓒ Ernesto's grandmother did not get to see the Statue of Liberty when she first arrived in the United States.

   Ⓓ Great-Uncle Harry left his mother behind in Russia to come to the United States.

3. Which of the following statements is true of the nonfiction piece? (MAKE CONNECTIONS STRATEGY)

   Ⓐ There is no mention of important dates.

   Ⓑ It shows characters in a story doing research.

   Ⓒ All the dates in the story are made up.

   Ⓓ It mentions only people who are real and events that really happened.

4. What other monuments have you read about or seen that meant something important to you? Pick one to write about on the lines below. Tell what is important about it. (MAKE CONNECTIONS STRATEGY)

   _____

   _____

   _____

   _____

   _____

   _____

   _____

A MONUMENTAL MYSTERY

A MIGHTY Woman

5. On the lines below, write a description that would help someone coming from another country to New York City for the first time to recognize the Statue of Liberty. Include details from both selections.

_____

_____

_____

_____

_____

_____

_____

_____

_____

_____

_____

_____

_____

STOP This is the end of the test.